Physics 1a — Energy

Pages 1-2 — Heat Radiation

Q1 a) i) True
  ii) True
  iii) False
  iv) True
  v) False
  b) Hot objects do absorb infrared radiation.
Cold objects do emit infrared radiation (but much less than hot objects).

Q2 a) Dark, matt surfaces are **good** absorbers and **good** emitters of infrared radiation.
  b) The best surfaces for radiating infrared are **good** absorbers and **good** emitters.
  c) Silvered surfaces are **poor** absorbers and **poor** emitters of infrared radiation.
  d) The best surfaces for solar hot water panels are **good** absorbers and **good** emitters.

Q3 a) Infrared radiation is emitted from the **surface** of hot solid objects **and** from liquids and gases.
  b) **All** objects absorb infrared radiation — the bigger the difference in temperature between an object and its surroundings, the **faster** the rate of heat transfer.

Q4 So they lose as little heat energy as possible by radiation (shiny surfaces are poor emitters).

Q5 a) False
  b) True
  c) True
  d) False
  e) True

Q6 Flask B will cool fastest because there is a larger temperature difference between the water and the air in the box.

Q7 E.g. Paint the radiator matt black. Put a shiny inner surface between the radiator and the roof. Put a glass (or similar) sheet in front of it. Use a different material for the radiator. Use a bigger radiator. Tilt the radiator so it faces straight at the Sun at noon.

Page 3 — Kinetic Theory

Q1

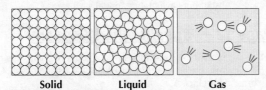

Solid   Liquid   Gas

Gas — There are almost no forces of attraction between the particles.
Liquid — There are weak forces of attraction between the particles.
Solid — There are strong forces of attraction holding the particles close together.

Q2 a) False
  b) True
  c) True
  d) True
  e) False

Q3 As you heat a solid, its particles will gain more kinetic energy. They will vibrate more and move faster and eventually overcome the strong forces of attraction that hold the particles in a solid together. Eventually the particles will move fast enough and far enough apart that the substance will become a liquid.

Page 4 — Co[n...]

Q1 a) True
  b) False
  c) True
  d) True

Q2 The piece of wood feels quite warm because wood is a poor conductor, so it does not conduct much heat energy away from George's hand. The metal spoon feels colder because metal is a good conductor, so it conducts heat energy away from his hand very quickly.

Q3 a) Insulator
  b) Conductor
  c) Conductor
  d) Conductor

Q4 a) Copper is a good conductor because it's got free electrons in it. All materials contain electrons, but if they're not free electrons they don't help conduction.
  b) Colour and shininess don't make any difference to conduction. Mamphela is getting mixed up with radiation, where it does make a difference.
  c) All the particles in all materials have kinetic energy. Ruth doesn't explain that the free electrons mean that kinetic energy is able to move about so easily in copper.

Pages 5-6 — Convection

Q1 a) i) True
  ii) False
  iii) True
  iv) False
  b) ii) The colder the water, the denser it is. (Note: this is only true above 4 °C. Below 4 °C, water gets less dense as it cools.)
  iv) Convection currents can happen in any liquid or gas.

Q2 The very bottom of a hot water tank stays cold... because water doesn't conduct much heat.
Warm air rises... because it is not so dense.
A small heater can send heat all over a room... because heat flows from warm places to cooler ones.

Q3 a) The particles gain more energy as heat is transferred from the radiator to the air.
  b) The particles have more energy so move around faster. The distance between them becomes greater, so the air expands and becomes less dense. This reduction in density means the hotter air rises above the cooler, denser air.

Q4 a)

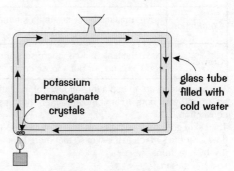

potassium permanganate crystals

glass tube filled with cold water

  b) The water is heated by conduction.
The temperature of the water increases.
The water expands (as its temperature increases).
The water becomes less dense (as it expands as the particles get further apart).
The warm water floats upwards and is replaced by denser cold water from the right.

Q5 The experiment shows that convection works very well in water — the ice melts because convection currents carry warm water upwards. It also shows that water is a poor **conductor** of heat — convection currents do not warm the water below the flame, and the water below the heater stays cold because conduction only occurs very slowly.

Physics 1a — Energy

Page 7 — Condensation and Evaporation

Q1 liquid, cools, kinetic energy, attractive.
Q2 a) i) True
ii) False
iii) False
b) ii) Particles can evaporate from a liquid at temperatures much lower than the liquid's boiling point.
iii) The speed of a particle, its mass, the direction it's travelling in and how near the surface it is all affect whether it can escape a liquid.
Q3 Sweating cools you down — when the sweat on your skin evaporates it causes a cooling effect. This is because the fastest particles (the ones with most kinetic energy) are most likely to evaporate from a liquid (the sweat). When they do, the average speed and kinetic energy of the remaining particles decreases. This decrease in average particle energy means the temperature of the remaining liquid falls. Sweating more will increase this cooling effect, as more particles will evaporate from skin.
Q4 a) E.g. if the liquid has a high temperature, low density, large surface area and if there is a low concentration of the liquid in the air it's evaporating into.
b) E.g. if the temperature of the surface the gas touches is lower, if the surface area of the surface the gas touches is larger.

Pages 8-9 — Rate of Heat Transfer

Q1 a) To maximise the amount of heat transfer.
b) Metal is a good conductor so it will conduct heat away from the radiator much faster than air, as air is an insulator.
Q2 Any four from:
Shiny surfaces — reduce radiation.
Insulating foam supports — reduce conduction.
Vacuum gap between walls of bottle — reduce conduction and convection.
Stopper made of poor conductors, e.g. plastic — reduces conduction.
Air space between bottle and outer case — reduces conduction.
Outer case made of plastic — reduces conduction.
Q3 E.g.

	Suggested Improvements
Radiation	Make the outside surface shiny / white / silvery.
Conduction	Cover the tank with 'lagging' material that conducts poorly, e.g. fibreglass.
Convection	Have the tank in a cupboard so warm air can't 'escape', or put a loose cover over it.

Q4 a) The hairs 'stand up' to trap a thicker layer of insulating air around your body to limit the amount of heat lost by convection.
b) Their skin goes pink as the body diverts more blood to flow near the surface of the skin so that more heat can be lost by radiation.
Q5 a) i) Fox A — desert.
ii) Fox B — Arctic.
b) Large ears give a large surface area for Fox A to lose heat from easily by radiation. This helps Fox A avoid overheating in a hot climate. Fox B's small ears give a small surface area to minimise heat loss by radiation and stay warm in a cold climate.
Q6 a) Reading down the table: 3 : 1, 1.5 : 1, 1 : 1, 0.75 : 1, 0.6 : 1.
b) The surface area : volume ratio decreases as the size of the cube increases.
c) The small cube, because it has a small volume where it can hold heat but a relatively large surface over which it can lose it.

d) Fins increase the surface area of the car engine so it has a larger surface area to volume ratio. This means heat will be radiated away quicker so the engine cools quicker.

Pages 10-11 — Energy Efficiency in the Home

Q1 a) Through the roof — loft insulation.
Through the walls — cavity wall insulation.
Through the doors — double glazing of any glass panels, draught-proofing strips around the frames and letter box.
b) She could install double glazing, fit draught-proofing strips around the windows, and have thick curtains. (Or she could turn her heating down.)
Q2 a) Cavity wall insulation — reduces heat transfer by convection, because pockets of air are trapped in the foam, and can't move between the two walls. The foam and air pockets trapped inside it are both insulators, so heat transfer by conduction is reduced. It also reduces radiation across the gap.
b) Loft insulation — layers of fibreglass wool reduce heat transfer by conduction from the ceiling to the roof space. Heat transfer out of the house by convection is also reduced.
Q3 a) Payback time = 1200 ÷ 20 = 60 years.
b) No, because although the shutters are cheaper, they are less cost-effective — they have a longer payback time.
Q4 a) U-values measure how effective a material is as an insulator.
b) Gary should choose brand A because it has a lower U-value — the lower the U-value, the better the material is as an insulator, so heat transfer will be less.
Q5 a) Shona is right — a method that pays for itself faster will start saving you money sooner.
Alison is right — good value means getting a good effect from the money spent.
Tim is wrong — cheap or badly installed insulation might not work very well.
Meena is wrong — cost-effectiveness means getting a good energy saving per pound spent.
b) If you plan to move house soon, it makes sense to choose a method with a short payback time. But if you stay in the house for 20 years, say, you would save more in the long term by choosing a method which might cost more to install but gave higher annual savings.

Page 12 — Specific Heat Capacity

Q1 a) Specific heat capacity is the amount of energy needed to raise the temperature of 1 kg of a substance by 1 °C.
b) Substance A
Q2 a) Concrete
b) Water is used because it has a really high specific heat capacity so it can store large amounts of heat, and can be easily pumped around pipes.
Q3 Energy = Mass × SHC × temperature change.
The temperature change for both is 50 °C.
Energy from mercury = 27.2 × 139 × 50 = 189 040 J.
Energy from water = 2 × 4200 × 50 = 420 000 J.
Difference = 420 000 − 189 040 = **230 960 J** (≈ 231 kJ).
Q4 Rearrange the energy equation:
Mass = Energy ÷ (SHC × temperature change).
Mass = 3040 ÷ (380 × 40) = 3040 ÷ 15 200
= **0.2 kg** of copper (or **200 g**).

Pages 13-14 — Energy Transfer

Q1 conservation, transferred, dissipated, created.
Q2 a) **chemical energy** → heat and light energy.
b) electrical energy → **sound and heat energy**.
c) **electrical energy** → **light and heat energy**.

GCSE

Physics

Exam Board: AQA

Answer Book

Contents

Published by CGP

ISBN: 978 1 84762 629 5

www.cgpbooks.co.uk

Printed by Elanders Ltd, Newcastle upon Tyne.
Clipart from Corel®

Based on the classic CGP style created by Richard Parsons.

Physics 1a — Energy

Q3 a) i) chemical energy
ii) heat/thermal energy (and kinetic energy)
b) Any two from:
Chemical energy → heat energy (as the coal burns).
Heat energy → kinetic energy (as the steam drives the engine).
Chemical energy → light energy (in the lamp).
Other answers are possible.

Q4 a) Gravitational potential energy.
b) Chemical energy from the porridge is transferred to kinetic energy in Bruce's muscles and the moving bar. This kinetic energy is then transferred to gravitational potential energy.
c) The gravitational potential energy is transferred into kinetic energy as it falls downwards.

Q5 Electric fan — kinetic energy
Iron — heat energy
Bedside table lamp — light energy

Q6 1. Chemical energy from the archer's food is stored in his muscles.
2. Chemical energy in the archer's muscles is transferred into elastic potential energy.
3. Energy stored in the pulled bow and string is transferred into kinetic energy.
4. As it goes upwards the arrow loses kinetic energy and gains gravitational potential energy.
5. The arrow loses gravitational potential energy and gains kinetic energy as it falls to earth.

Q7 a) In a battery-powered torch, the battery transfers **chemical** energy into **electrical** energy OR the **bulb** transfers electrical energy into light energy.
b) A wind turbine transfers kinetic energy into electrical energy **and heat and sound energy**.
c) A wind-up toy car transfers **elastic potential energy** into kinetic energy and sound energy.

Q8 a) E.g. loudspeaker or buzzer/bell.
b) Solar cell/photovoltaic cell.
c) E.g. hair dryer or electric fan heater.

Pages 15-17 — Efficiency of Machines

Q1 transfer, useful, heat, fraction, input, output.
Q2 a) 100 J
b) 5 J
c) 95 J
Q3

	Total Energy Input (J)	Useful Energy Output (J)	Efficiency
1	2000	1500	**0.75 (or 75%)**
2	**4000**	2000	0.50
3	4000	**1000**	0.25

Q4 Useful power output = efficiency × total power input
= 0.9 × 2000 = 1800 W.

Q5 The winch, like all other devices, is not 100% efficient. 10 J of the 20 J of input energy was 'wasted'. Much of this waste was likely to have been heat energy, generated by friction and electrical resistance in the motor, and between the moving parts of the winch.

Q6 a) By seeing how long each MP3 player can run before the batteries run out. Comparing the times is equivalent to comparing the useful energy outputs (the useful energy output will be proportional to the time).
b) Any two from:
Play the same music, play (the same) music at the same volume, use the same number/type of batteries.
c) Player B is more efficient than player A. In fact player B is one-third more efficient than player A (or player A is only three-quarters as efficient as B).

Q7 A heat exchanger can be used to transfer some of the waste heat energy from the car's engine to the air that's used to warm the passenger compartment.

Q8 a) Any two from:
Longer life.
Cheaper to run OR uses less energy/electricity.
Cheaper to buy per year of its lifetime.
(Or other sensible answers.)
b) Any two from:
Cheaper to buy.
Bright as soon as you switch it on.
Low-energy bulbs can't be used with dimmer switches.
(Or other sensible answers.)

Pages 18-19 — Energy Transformation Diagrams

Q1 a) 10 J.
b) 150 J.
Q2 See diagram below — where the scale is 1 small square = 2 J. Different scales are possible.

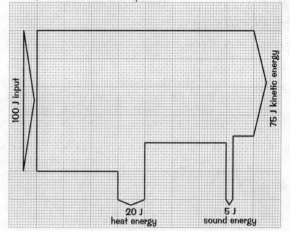

Q3 1. The input energy is not shown clearly.
The 100 J kinetic energy should be shown as input energy.
2. The quantities of energy do not add up. The electrical energy plus the waste heat energy should equal the input energy. Either the input should be 175 J, or the heat wasted should be 25 J. (Or all the values are wrong).

Q4 a) 100 J heat + 40 J GPE = 140 J
b) 60 J
c) Efficiency = 60 ÷ 200 = 0.3.

Pages 20-21 — The Cost of Electricity

Q1 a) Energy used = 2 kW × 3 hours = **6 kWh**.
b) Cost of energy = 14p/kWh × 6 kWh = **84p**.
Q2 Energy used = 0.1 kW × 10 h = 1 kWh, so the cost is **11.3p**.
Q3 A 60 W lamp on for 9 h uses 0.06 × 9 = **0.54 kWh**.
An 8 kW shower on for 0.25 h uses 8 × 0.25 = **2 kWh**.
So Tina is right — the shower uses nearly four times as much energy as the lamp.
Q4 a) 34783 – 34259 = **524 kWh**.
b) 524 × 9.7p = 5083p (to nearest penny) = **£50.83**.
Q5 a) Number of kWh used = 7 × 275 × 1000
= 1 925 000 kWh so cost = kWh × night time cost per kWh
= 1 925 000 × 3.7 = 7 122 500p or **£71 225**.
b) kWh generated = 5 × 288 × 1000 = 1 440 000 kWh so cost
= kWh × daytime cost per kWh
= 1 440 000 × 7.2 = 10 368 000 or **£103 680**.
Q6 Difference between meter readings on first night
= 13598.63 – 13592.42 = 6.21 kWh
Difference between meter readings on second night
= 13649.41 – 13646.68 = 2.73 kWh
Difference between energy usage on 1st and 2nd night
= 6.21 – 2.73 = **3.48 kWh**.

Physics 1b — Electricity and Waves

Page 22 — Choosing Electrical Appliances

Q1 E.g. It can be used in locations where there is no access to mains electricity. / It's easier to use as there is no power cord to get in the way/restrict movement.

Q2 a) Battery powered lamp: Energy used to fully charge (enough for 8 hours use) = 400 W × 6 hours = 2.4 kWh
Mains powered lamp: Energy used in 8 hours = 1.6 kW × 8 = 12.8 kWh
So, difference in energy used = 12.8 – 2.4 = **10.4 kWh**

b) Difference in cost = 10.4 × 12 = **124.8p**

c) E.g. There might not be an electricity supply where they are camping, so they will not be able to use a mains powered lamp or recharge the battery powered lamp when it runs out. The wind up lamp does not require any electricity to recharge.

Q3 E.g. any two from: can be used to power X-ray machines / refrigeration of medicines/vaccines / can power lighting/ equipment for operations / refrigeration of food.

Pages 23-25 — Mixed Questions — Physics 1a

Q1 a) Pockets of air are trapped in bubbles of foam, reducing convection and radiation across the gap. Air is an insulator, so it also reduces conduction.

b) Paul should look for a low U-value because materials with a low U-value are better insulators, so heat loss will be less.

c) The condensation happens because water vapour in the air cools as it comes into contact with the cold surface. As the vapour cools, the particles in it slow down and lose kinetic energy. The particles no longer have enough kinetic energy to overcome the attractive forces between them, so the vapour becomes a liquid.

Q2 a) E.g.

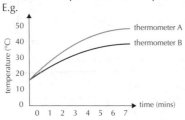

b) The matt black surface is a better absorber of heat radiation (from the Bunsen burner flame) than the shiny silver surface. The matt black surface is also a better emitter of radiation, so the temperature rise for A will be quicker/steeper than for B.

c) chemical energy → heat, light energy and sound energy

Q3 a) The freezer compartment cools the warmer air at the top of the fridge, which then falls, forcing warmer air to rise.

b) Energy (in kWh) = Power (in kW) × Time (in h)
= 0.5 kW × 24 h = 12 kWh.
Cost = No. of units × price per unit
= 12 kWh × 15p = **180p** (= £1.80)

Q4 a) Hot water tank jacket.

b) Over 5 years, the savings would be:
Hot water tank jacket: (5 × £15) – £15 = £60
Draught-proofing: (5 × £65) – £70 = £255
Cavity wall insulation: (5 × £70) – £560 = –£210
Thermostatic controls: (5 × £25) – £120 = £5.
So **draught-proofing** would save the most money.

c) The temperature change required is 36 – 14 = 22 °C.
Energy = mass × SHC × change in temperature
= 90 × 4200 × 22 = **8 316 000 J** (= 8316 kJ = 8.316 MJ).

Q5 a) Chemical energy.

b) E.g. below, using a scale of 1 small square = 25 joules. Other scales are possible.

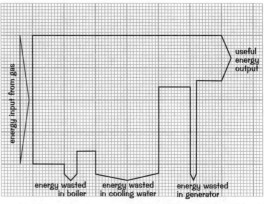

c) Useful output energy = 1000 J – 100 J – 500 J – 50 J = 350 J. So efficiency = 350 ÷ 1000 = **0.35** (or 35%).

Q6 a) Fins increase the surface area of the heat sink — a larger surface area means they emit heat quickly.

b) i) Metals are good conductors of heat because they have free electrons which can quickly transfer energy.

ii) The free electrons at the hot end move faster and collide with other free electrons, transferring energy. These other electrons then pass on their extra energy to other electrons, and so on across the piece of metal.

Physics 1b — Electricity and Waves

Page 26 — Energy Sources & Power Stations

Q1 1. Coal is burned to release heat.
2. Water is heated in a boiler and turned to steam.
3. Hot steam rushes through a turbine and makes it spin.
4. The spinning turbine makes the generator spin too.
5. Electricity is produced by the spinning generator.

Q2 a) Nuclear fission produces heat.

b) Non-renewable sources will eventually run out / cannot be replaced when they are used up.

Q3 Most power stations use **non-renewable** sources of energy, such as coal, oil or gas. These **fossil** fuels are initially burnt in a boiler. This converts the **chemical** energy in the fuel to **heat** energy. A turbine then converts this energy into **kinetic** energy, which, in turn is converted to **electrical** energy by a generator. This energy feeds into the national grid ready to be distributed to consumers.

Q4 Wind and solar power are unreliable as they depend on appropriate weather conditions to generate power. Whereas fossil fuels can be burnt all the time.

Page 27 — Renewable Energy Sources (1)

Q1 a) Any three from: they make a lot of noise, they spoil the view/landscape / cause visual pollution, they harm wildlife / they kill birds, they only work if it's windy, the electricity they generate is expensive, a lot of turbines are needed to replace one power station.

b) Any three from: once running, there's no permanent damage to the landscape, they use a renewable, free source of energy, running costs are low, they don't release greenhouse gases into the atmosphere.

Q2 Disadvantages — the initial costs are high, and most solar cells are not very efficient, they don't work well when it's cloudy. Advantages — they use a renewable and free source of energy (there are no fuel costs), they are a good way to provide energy in remote places, there is no pollution when they are in use.

Q3 a) They're a good source of energy in situations where only a small amount of electricity is needed, e.g. calculators. They're often available in places where there is no access to mains electricity, e.g. remote road signs.

b) The cost of connecting the remote farm to the National Grid would be enormous compared with the value of the electricity generated.

Pages 28-29 — Renewable Energy Sources (2)

Q1 a) Measurements provide more information than observations. The voltage gives a more accurate idea of how much energy was transferred.

b) Their results **do not support** their prediction because the relationship is not proportional — e.g. halving the height (200 cm to 100 cm) does not halve the voltage (0.2 V is not half of 1.1 V).

Q2 1. At night big power stations make more electricity than is needed.
2. Spare electricity is used to pump water from reservoirs at a low level to others at a high level.
3. Water at a high level stores energy until it is needed.
4. At peak times, when demand is the highest, water is allowed to flow downhill, powering turbines and generating electricity.

Q3 Big coal-fired power stations deliver energy... all the time.
Pumped storage power stations deliver energy... that they have previously stored / when it is needed.
Hydroelectric power stations deliver electricity... when it is needed.

Q4 a) The student could say that no atmospheric pollution is produced when electricity is being generated, or that building the dams and manufacturing the turbines, generators etc. does cause atmospheric pollution/or that the power plant will cause both visual and noise pollution.

b) The student could say that there are no fuel costs, or that building dams and purchasing turbines etc. is expensive.

c) The student might argue that dams are unsightly, they disturb the natural environment, and disrupt / destroy wildlife habitats etc., or they could argue that an impressive engineering structure has a positive visual impact, and/or that not all hydroelectric projects involve building dams.

d) The student could say that it is rare for reservoirs to be empty even in dry weather, and water can be released to power the generators when it's needed most, or they could say that power supplies are less reliable during droughts, and this may be a more serious problem in the future.

e) Any two from: it is a renewable source of energy, it does not contribute to global warming (once running), the output can be varied more quickly than that of most other power stations, good for use in remote locations.

f) Any two from: rotting vegetation releases greenhouse gases (methane and CO_2) when the valley is flooded, set-up costs are high, set-up times are long, destruction of wildlife habitats.

Page 30 — Renewable Energy Sources (3)

Q1 a) Tidal.
b) Wave.
c) Tidal.
d) Wave.
e) Tidal.

Q2 a) When the tide comes in the water passes through the turbines and then builds up behind the barrage. When the tide goes out the water is allowed out through the turbines in the barrage at a controlled speed. As the water passes through the turbines electricity is generated. (The water also turns the turbines on the way in.)

b) Any two from the following: Initial costs are fairly high. Barrages can look unattractive. Barrages can prevent access for boats. Barrages can damage habitats. The height of tides is variable. No energy is available at the turn of the tides.

Q3 a) 1. A wave moves water upwards, forcing air out towards a turbine.
2. The moving air makes the turbine spin.
3. The spinning turbine drives a generator.
4. The spinning generator makes electricity.
5. The water goes down again.
6. Air is sucked downwards, spinning the turbine the other way and generating more power.

b) Any two from the following: High initial costs. Spoiling the view. Can be unreliable because it depends on winds. It is currently only suitable for small-scale use. Can be a hazard to boats.

Page 31 — Renewable Energy Sources (4)

Q1 Biofuels are used to generate electricity in a similar way to **fossil fuels**. Biofuels are burnt to heat **water** and make **steam**, which is used to drive **turbines** to power generators and make electricity.
Biofuels can be solids (e.g. **woodchips**), liquids (e.g. **ethanol**) or gases (e.g. **methane**).

Q2 In some volcanic areas, hot water and steam rise to the surface. This steam can be used to drive turbines to generate electricity.

Q3 Biofuels will not run out — more can always be made to us as a source of energy.

Q4 a) False
b) False
c) False
d) True

Page 32 — Energy Sources and the Environment

Q1 Acid rain... sulfur dioxide formed by burning oil and coal.
Climate change... releasing CO_2 by burning fossil fuels.
Dangerous radioactive waste... using nuclear power.
Spoiling of natural landscapes... coal mining OR sulfur dioxide formed by burning oil and coal.

Q2 Answer will depend on student's opinion but should include an explanation of their reasoning, e.g. Lisa because nuclear power produces long-lasting, dangerous, radioactive waste. Or Ben because nuclear power is carefully controlled to reduce any dangers. Also, nuclear power doesn't produce any carbon dioxide, whereas using fossil fuels adds to the carbon dioxide in the atmosphere, leading to climate change / an increased greenhouse effect / global warming.

Q3 Plants that are used to produce biofuels (or to feed animals that produce biofuels) absorb carbon dioxide from the atmosphere. Burning the biofuel puts the carbon back into the atmosphere as carbon dioxide, so overall there is a neutral effect on the atmosphere.

Q4 a) This is the process of collecting carbon dioxide from power stations before it is released into the atmosphere.

b) E.g. in empty gas fields, oil fields, dissolved in seawater at the bottom of the ocean, capturing with algae.

Pages 33-34 — Comparison of Energy Resources

Q1 Gas
Q2 a) Any one of: gas supplies often need to be imported and there may be steep price rises, gas will run out eventually, burning gas causes atmospheric pollution and contributes to the global warming. Other answers are possible.

b) Any one of: high set-up costs, high maintenance and/or decommissioning costs, long set-up times, dangerous radioactive waste, risk of catastrophic accidents, threat from terrorism, nuclear fuels need to be imported. Other answers are possible.

Physics 1b — Electricity and Waves

c) Any one of: it's dependent on the weather / only works when the wind is blowing, unreliable, visual pollution / spoils the view, noise pollution. Other answers are possible.

d) E.g. high set-up costs. Other answers are possible.

Q3 a) Most (about 75%) of the UK's electricity generation depends on supplies of coal, oil and gas. These fuels are all non-renewable and will run out eventually.

b) 1. We don't know how to dispose of the radioactive waste safely.
2. Nuclear power stations and radioactive waste are targets for terrorists.

c) Shutting down / removing from active status.

d) Answer will depend on student's opinion. 'I agree' could be backed up by mentioning that sea levels change in a predictable and reliable way, twice every day, and/or that the UK has a long coastline and plenty of opportunities to use the resource. 'I disagree' could be backed up by saying that there are only a few suitable estuaries, or that at neap tides, the difference in sea level between low and high tides is small, so there is not much energy available.

e) E.g. Any two from: it's a reliable source of energy, it doesn't release greenhouse gases, we're not likely to run out of uranium any time soon (and some of the waste can be reprocessed and reused).

Pages 35-36 — Electricity and the National Grid

Q1 1. Electrical energy is generated in power stations.
2. The voltage of the supply is raised.
3. An electrical current flows through power cables across the country.
4. The voltage of the supply is reduced.
5. Mrs Miggins boils the kettle for tea.

Q2 a) Underground cables
b) Overhead cables
c) Overhead cables
d) Overhead cables
e) Underground cables
f) Overhead cables
g) Underground cables

Q3 a) Step-up transformer, pylons, step-down transformer, insulators.

b) At higher voltages, less energy is wasted as heat. This saves more money than the cost of the equipment.

Q4 a) The National Grid transmits energy at high voltage and **low current**.

b) A step-up transformer is used to **increase** the voltage of the supply (OR reduce the **current**) before electricity is transmitted.

c) Using a **low current** (OR high **voltage**) makes sure there is not much energy wasted.

Q5 a) Supply is the amount of electricity generated and delivered to consumers. Demand is the amount of electricity needed by the consumers.

b) Consumer demand for energy is increasing, so the National Grid has to increase the supply to meet this demand.

c) E.g. More plants can be built, power output of power plants can be increased.

d) E.g. Use energy efficient appliances, being more careful not to waste energy in the home (e.g. by turning off lights).

Pages 37-38 — Wave Basics

Q1 energy, matter

Q2 a) Transverse — 2, Longitudinal — 1.

b) E.g. transverse waves can travel in a vacuum but longitudinal waves cannot / vibrations in a transverse wave are perpendicular to the direction of energy transfer, whereas in longitudinal waves they are parallel to the direction of energy transfer.

Q3 a) A and C
b) A and B
c) A and C

Q4 Transverse
vibrations are at 90° to the direction of energy transfer
produced by a slinky spring whose end is wiggled at 90° to the spring itself
ripples on water
electromagnetic radiation
Longitudinal
vibrations are along the same direction as the energy transfer
sound waves
produced by a slinky spring whose end is pushed and pulled towards and away from the rest of the spring

Q5 a) metres
b) There are 25 waves per second.
c) A

Q6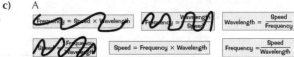

Q7 You need to work out the frequency.
Using $v = f\lambda$ and rearranging gives
frequency = speed ÷ wavelength.
So frequency = $(3 \times 10^8) \div (5 \times 10^{-7}) = \mathbf{6 \times 10^{14}\,Hz}$.

Q8 a) He has drawn a wave with a wavelength of 4 m rather than 2 m.

b)

Q9 You need to work out the wavelength.
Using $v = f\lambda$ and rearranging gives:
wavelength = speed ÷ frequency.
So wavelength = $(3 \times 10^8) \div (4.6 \times 10^{15}) = \mathbf{6.5 \times 10^{-8}\,m}$

Page 39 — Wave Properties

Q1 a) The normal is an imaginary line that's at right angles to the surface at the point of incidence (where the light hits the surface).

b)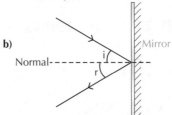

Q2 a)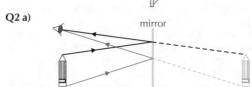

b) virtual
c) upright

Physics 1b — Electricity and Waves

d) The left and right hand side of the object are swapped round in the image. E.g. the right hand side of the actual pencil appears to be the left hand side of the pencil on the image.

Page 40 — Refraction and Diffraction

Q1 a) Diffraction is the spreading out of waves when they pass through a gap or past an obstacle.

b)

Q2 a) B

b) Waves don't refract when they're travelling along the normal.

c) When a wave changes direction as it hits the boundary between two different media.

Q3 The gap is too wide. The gap needs to be of similar magnitude (size) to the wavelength of the wave.

Pages 41-42 — EM Waves and Communication

Q1 a)

Radio waves	Micro-waves	Infrared			Ultraviolet	X-rays	Gamma rays
1m-10⁴m	10⁻²m (1 cm)	10⁻⁵m (0.01mm)		10⁻⁷m	10⁻⁸m	10⁻¹⁰m	10⁻¹⁵m

b) The energy of the waves **increases** from **left to right** across the table.

Q2 a) i) False
ii) False
iii) False
iv) True
b) i) Visible light travels **at the same speed** in a vacuum **as** both X-rays and radio waves.
ii) All EM waves transfer **energy** from place to place.
iii) Radio waves have the **longest** wavelength of all EM waves.

Q3 A, B and C

Q4 EM waves with higher frequencies have **shorter** wavelengths. The **higher** the frequency of an EM wave, the greater the energy of the wave.

Q5 The house can receive **long-wave** signals because they can diffract around the mountain. It also receives **short-wave** signals because they are reflected by the **ionosphere**. However **FM** signals are not received at the house as the transmitter is not in direct line of sight of the house.

Q6 Things they have in common — any two from: they can both travel in a vacuum, they both travel at the speed of light, they both transfer energy.
(Or other sensible answers.)
Ways in which they differ — any two from: they have different wavelengths, they have different frequencies, they have different energies.
(Or other sensible answers.)

Pages 43-44 — EM Waves and Their Uses

Q1 Infrared
Q2 a) This allows the satellite to send signals to (and receive signals from) a large area of the Earth.
b) Radio waves can't pass easily through the earth's watery atmosphere.
c) Microwaves
Q3 a) Visible light or infrared waves.
b) They are reflected down the core of the fibre.
Q4 The microwaves are not absorbed or reflected much by the water molecules in clouds (unlike visible light).
Q5 a) Microwaves
b) Their brain cells may be heated up and damaged.

c) E.g. convenience (e.g. keeping in touch with friends), safety (they feel the positives outweigh the risks). Also many people only use their phones for short periods of time, so they have limited exposure.
Q6 E.g. The lens focuses the light onto a light sensitive film or electronic sensor. The film or sensor then records the image.

Pages 45-46 — Sound Waves

Q1 C, A, D, B.
Q2 vibrate, high, low.
Q3 The bigger the **amplitude** of a sound wave, the **louder** the sound.
Q4 2000
Q5 a) 30 Hz
b) 5 Hz, 630 Hz, 8 kHz, 21 kHz, 400 kHz, 3 MHz
Q6 a) A reflected sound wave.
b) The soft surfaces in her bedroom absorb the sound vibrations better, so less sound is reflected around the room.
c) The echoed sound has to travel further, and so takes longer to reach your ears.
Q7 a) It gets quieter and eventually stops. Because sound is a vibration passed from molecule to molecule, it cannot be transmitted through a vacuum.
b) The foam prevents the sound from being transmitted through the solid surface that the clock is placed on.

Pages 47-48 — The Origin of the Universe

Q1 a) It will sound lower pitched.
b) Doppler effect
c) The wavelength seems to increase.
d) The frequency would seem to have increased.
Q2 As the train leaves, it moves away from Brian's microphone. So the frequency appears to get slightly **lower**. E.g.

Q3 Light from other galaxies is red-shifted — all the frequencies are lower in the spectrum than is the case for other objects nearby. This tells us that the galaxies are moving away from us. Also, the further away the galaxy, the greater the red-shift. This tells us that more distant galaxies are moving away from us at a faster rate than nearer galaxies.
Q4 a) The universe started as a single point that exploded in the Big Bang and has been expanding ever since.
b) Space itself is expanding.
Q5 a) Low frequency electromagnetic radiation coming from all parts of the universe.
b) Very shortly after the beginning of the universe, the universe was very hot and emitted very high energy, high frequency radiation. As the universe expanded it cooled, and this radiation dropped in frequency and is now detected as the CMBR.
Q6 E.g. Any one from: It can't explain observed acceleration and expansion of the universe. / It doesn't tell you anything about the universe before the Big Bang.

Pages 49-52 — Mixed Questions — Physics 1b

Q1 a) B represents ultraviolet radiation.
The infrared wave has the largest amplitude.
b) B — They are all transverse waves.
D — They all travel at the same speed in space.
Q2 a) i) E.g. Solar cells require little maintenance and no fuel, making them suitable for remote locations (where transporting fuel and arranging repairs would be difficult and expensive). Solar power is a renewable source of energy and won't pollute the island.

Physics 2a — Motion, Energy and Electricity

ii) E.g. The island is likely to be quite windy. Wind turbines are fairly cheap to install. As with solar power, wind power is renewable, doesn't cause pollution and doesn't require fuel.

b) Wave power — around the coastline, biomass — llama poo could be used to produce biofuel for burning. (Hydroelectric power might also be possible, depending on the island's geography and climate.)

Q3 a) Frequency = speed ÷ wavelength = 3×10^8 m/s ÷ 1500 m = **200 000 Hz** (= 200 kHz).

b) Longer waves diffract more around large objects than shorter waves. So the long-wave radio signal diffracts around the mountains and can be received in Mr Potts' holiday cottage. The TV signal is short-wave so it doesn't diffract much and can't be received in his cottage.

Q4 a) E.g. it's clean / fuel is relatively cheap / it's reliable

b) Carbon capture and storage technology is used to collect CO_2 from fossil-fuel power stations before it is released into the atmosphere. This reduces the amount of CO_2 building up in the atmosphere and reduces the strength of the greenhouse effect.

Q5 a) reflection

b)

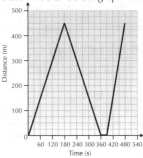

TV remote sensor

mirror

normal

TV remote

angle of incidence, i = angle of reflection, r

Q6 a) The 'spare' electricity can be used to pump water up to a higher reservoir, which can then be released quickly during periods of peak demand to generate electricity.

b) E.g. increase supply by opening more power plants, increase supply by increasing the power output of power plants, consumers reducing their demands.

Q7 a) Diffraction

b) It will diffract the most when the gap is the same size as the wavelength. If the gap is much wider than the wavelength, it will only diffract a little.

c) Water molecules can absorb some wavelengths of microwave. If the water in question happens to be in your cells, e.g. brain cells, this may cause cell damage / your brain might start to cook.

Q8 a) 0.02 m

b) 10 Hz

c) speed = wavelength × frequency = 0.02 × 10 = **0.2 m/s**

Q9 a) The gas is burned to convert its stored chemical energy into heat energy. The heat is used to turn water into steam, which drives turbines. Generators then convert the kinetic energy of the turbine blades into electrical energy.

b) i) nuclear energy, biofuel

ii) Both solar and wind power are unreliable / dependent on the weather. / On days which weren't sunny or windy, there would be little or no electricity.

c) i) So that the current required to transmit power can be low, which reduces the energy wasted through heating in the cables.

ii) The high voltage is 'stepped down' using a series of transformers before it reaches people's homes or businesses.

Q10 a)

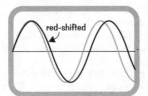

red-shifted

b) More distant galaxies have greater red-shifts than nearer ones, showing that more distant galaxies are moving away from us faster. This is evidence that the universe is expanding and started in a very dense (and hot) state.

Physics 2a — Motion, Energy and Electricity

Page 53 — Velocity and Distance-Time Graphs

Q1 −12 m/s

Q2 a) 180 s (or 3 mins)

b) Speed = gradient of graph = distance ÷ time
Speed = 450 ÷ 180 = 2.5 m/s

c) He runs there in half the time it took him to walk there — 90 s. So the graph looks like this:

Distance (m) / Time (s)

Q3 The graph shows that the motorist accelerates for about 1.5 seconds, then travels at a constant speed. So the gradient of the graph between 1.5 s and 3.0 s will give you the speed. Gradient = vertical change ÷ horizontal change = (72 − 18) ÷ (3.0 − 1.5) = 54 ÷ 1.5 = **36 m/s** — i.e. she was exceeding the speed limit. So the motorist wasn't telling the truth.

Pages 54-55 — Acceleration and Velocity-Time Graphs

Q1 a) The car accelerates from rest, so the change in velocity is **20 m/s**.
Acceleration = change in velocity ÷ time taken = 20 ÷ 3.5 = **5.7 m/s²**.

b) Change in velocity = 20 − 3 = 17 m/s.
So acceleration = 17 ÷ 2.8 = **6.1 m/s²**.
The car has a greater acceleration than before. (This assumes that the modified car's acceleration from 0 to 3 m/s is not slower.)

Q2 a) Since the egg was dropped from rest, its change in speed is 80 m/s. So acceleration = 80 ÷ 8 = **10 m/s²**.

b) Now rearrange the formula to get time taken
Time taken = change in velocity ÷ acceleration = 40 ÷ 10 = **4 s**

Q3 Rearranging the formula for acceleration you get:
change in speed = acceleration × time = 2 × 4 = 8 m/s.
Change in speed = final speed − initial speed,
so initial speed = final speed − change in speed = 24 − 8 = **16 m/s**.

Q4 Acceleration = gradient = 8 ÷ 5 = **1.6 m/s²**.

Q5 **A** — (constant) acceleration (from 0 - 3 m/s)
B — constant speed (of 3 m/s)
C — (constant) acceleration (from 3 - 9 m/s)
D — constant speed (of 9 m/s)
E — (constant) deceleration (from 9 - 7 m/s)

Physics 2a — Motion, Energy and Electricity

Q6 The distance the bus driver travelled before stopping is equal to the area under the graph. To find it, split the graph into a rectangle and a triangle.
Area of the rectangle = base × height = 0.75 × 12 = 9 m.
Area of the triangle = half × base × height = 0.5 × 2.5 × 12 = 15 m. Total distance = 9 m + 15 m = **24 m**.
He didn't hit the piglet.

Page 56 — Weight, Mass and Gravity

Q1 mass, kilograms, weight, newtons, gravitational

Q2 a) W = m × g
m = 58 kg, g = 10 N/kg
W = 58 × 10 = **580 N**

b) Change in weight = 580 – 460 = 120 N
Change in mass = change in weight ÷ g
= 120 ÷ 10 = **12 kg**

Q3a) Mass is the amount of matter, which stays constant. Weight is the force of gravity on this mass, and as the gravity is a different strength on Mars her weight changes.

b) Mass = weight ÷ gravitational field strength, which on Earth is 10 N/kg, so the rock has a mass of 5 kg.
1.9 kg ÷ 5 kg = 0.38
The scales read 38% of the true mass, so the gravitational field strength on Mars is 38% of that on Earth. 10 N/kg × 0.38 = **3.8 N/kg** (or m/s^2).

Page 57 — Resultant Forces

Q1 a) The teapot's weight is balanced by a reaction force from the table.

b) i) No. The teapot is accelerating so the forces can't be balanced.

ii) The reaction force from the floor.

Q2 a)

Reaction
Thrust
Drag / air resistance
Weight

b) No — he is decelerating. South.

Q3 a) 1 500 000 – 1 500 000 = 0 N

b) 6 000 000 – 1 500 000 = 4 500 000 N

Q4 a) There is a resultant force — the ball is slowing down, which is deceleration.

b) There is a resultant force — motion in a circle means constantly changing direction, which requires acceleration.

c) There is no resultant force — the vase is stationary on the window ledge.

Pages 58-60 — Forces and Acceleration

Q1 balanced, stationary, constant, non-zero, accelerates, resultant force, interact, opposite

Q2 The third statement should be ticked — The driving force of the engine is equal to friction and air resistance combined.

Q3 a) Statement **C** should be circled — The thrust is equal to the air resistance and the lift is equal to the weight.

b) i) The thrust is **less than** the air resistance.

ii) The lift is **less than** the weight.

Q4 Force = mass × acceleration.
Disraeli 9000: 800 kg × 5 m/s^2 = 4000 N
Palmerston 6i: 1560 kg × 0.7 m/s^2 = 1092 N
Heath TT: 950 kg × 3 m/s^2 = 2850 N
Asquith 380: 790 kg × 2 m/s^2 = 1580 N
So the correct order is: **Palmerston 6i, Asquith 380, Heath TT, Disraeli 9000.**

Q5 a) The force of the engine is 110 kg × 2.80 m/s^2 = **308 N**.

b) Mass = force ÷ acceleration = 308 ÷ 1.71 = **180 kg** (to 3 s.f.).

Q6 Using F = ma, the resultant force on the mass must be 1 kg × 0.25 m/s^2 = 0.25 N.
Resultant force = force on the newton-meter – force of friction (they act in opposite directions).
0.25 N = 0.4 N – force of friction, so force of friction = 0.4 N – 0.25 N = **0.15 N**.

Q7 The third statement should be ticked — The car's pulling force accelerates the caravan. The caravan's reaction acts on the car, not the caravan.

Q8 The first statement should be ticked — Your feet push backwards on the ground, so the ground pushes you forwards.

Q9a) i) The van is travelling at a steady speed, so the resultant force must be 0. So the force exerted by the engine must be equal to the air resistance and friction combined.
2000 N + 500 N = **2500 N**.

ii)

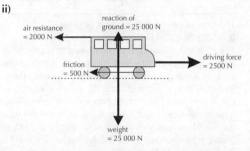

reaction of ground = 25 000 N
air resistance = 2000 N
friction = 500 N
driving force = 2500 N
weight = 25 000 N

b) The resultant force will now be 200 N (forces were previously balanced)
a = F/m = 200 ÷ 2500 = **0.08 m/s^2**.

c) The resultant force is now maximum driving force – (force of wind + friction + air resistance) = 2650 – 2700 = –50 N. This force acts in the opposite direction to the van's movement, so the van will continue to decelerate, but at a slower rate (0.02 m/s^2).

Pages 61-62 — Frictional Force and Terminal Velocity

Q1 greater, accelerates, increase, balances, constant, greater, decelerates, decrease, balances, constant.

Q2 All the boxes except 'carrying less cargo' should be ticked.

Q3 a) Paola is **wrong** because although gravity (the accelerating force per unit mass) is the same for both objects, air resistance will affect them differently because they have different shapes.

b) Guiseppe is **right** because drag will be greater for the feather compared to its weight, so drag will balance its weight sooner. The hammer will continue to accelerate for longer than the feather.

Q4 No, Mavis can't draw any conclusions.
The terminal velocity depends not only on drag (which is determined by the size, shape and smoothness of the object) but on the weight of the object, and the weights of the balls will be different.

Q5 Region A: weight is greater
Region B: both equal
Region C: air resistance is greater
Region D: both equal

Q6 a) No, Kate isn't really moving upwards. She only **seems** to move upwards when she opens her parachute because she slows down relative to the camera (which is held by Alison — who hasn't opened her parachute yet).

b) She decelerates until she reaches her terminal velocity and then falls at this speed until she lands.

Q7 a) Venus's atmosphere is much thicker than Earth's so a parachute the same size or smaller would provide enough drag to slow the probe to a safe speed.

Physics 2a — Motion, Energy and Electricity

b) Mars has lower gravity, so less drag is required to balance the probe's weight, but there is much less resistance from the thinner atmosphere, so the parachute would have to be larger than one used on Earth.

Page 63 — Stopping Distances

Q1 a) The distance the car travels under the braking force before it comes to a stop.

b) The distance the car travels during the driver's reaction time.

Q2

Thinking Distance	Braking Distance
tiredness alcohol speed drugs	road surface tyres weather brakes speed load

Q3 The total stopping distance will increase. Both thinking and braking distance will increase.

Q4 The friction between the brake discs and pads will be reduced if they are covered in water. This means the braking force will be reduced and the car will take longer to stop (i.e. the braking distance increases).

Q5 E.g. distractions like mobile phones won't affect Sam's thinking distance, as thinking distance is the distance travelled between the driver first spotting a hazard and taking action. However, it will mean that she will be less likely to notice a hazard until she is much closer to it. (So she is much more likely to crash if there is a hazard.)

Pages 64-65 — Work and Potential Energy

Q1 a) Work done and energy transferred are the same thing, so Jenny does **50 J** of work.

b) Distance = work done ÷ force = 50 ÷ 250 = **0.2 m**

Q2 To push your bicycle you need to apply a force to overcome resistant forces like friction. The work done is equal to the force you apply (in the direction of motion) multiplied by the distance you push your bike.

Q3 a) True

b) False

c) True

d) True

e) False ($E_p = m \times g \times h = 3 \times 10 \times 2.5 = $ **75 J**)

Q4 a) $E_p = m \times g \times h = 25$ kg $\times$ 10 N/kg $\times$ 1.2 m = **300 J**.

b) Total $E_p = 28 \times 300$ J = **8400 J**.

c) The energy transferred and the work done by Dave are the same thing, so **8400 J**.

Q5 a) Distance = work done ÷ force = 80 000 ÷ 50 N = **1600 m**

b) i) Work = force × distance, so force = work ÷ distance = 90 000 ÷ 120 = **750 N**. weight / gravity

ii) Work = gravitational potential energy = mass × g × height, so mass = work ÷ (g × height) mass = 90 000 ÷ (10 × 120) = **75 kg** (OR: Weight = mass × g so mass = weight ÷ g = 750 ÷10 = **75 kg**)

Q6 a) Rearrange E_p = mass × g × height: height = E_p ÷ (m × g) = 4000 ÷ (50 × 10) = 8 m

b) The energy converted from potential energy to kinetic energy is 1500 J, so the difference must be the wasted energy. 4000 J – 1500 J = **2500 J**.

c) friction

d) Force = work ÷ distance = 2500 ÷ 50 = **50 N**

e) Energy wasted = 4000 J – 2000 J = **2000 J**. Force = 2000 ÷ 50 = **40 N**

f) The mat reduces the amount of friction. Less energy is wasted and so more potential energy is converted into kinetic energy.

g) Force = 2000 ÷ 5 = **400 N**

Page 66 — Kinetic Energy

Q1 a) true

b) false

c) true

Q2 a) Just before the ball hits the ground, it has converted all of its potential energy into kinetic energy, so it has **242 J** of kinetic energy.

b) $v = \sqrt{\dfrac{2 \times E_k}{m}} = \sqrt{\dfrac{2 \times 242}{0.1}} = 69.6$ m/s

Q3 a) i) $v = \sqrt{\dfrac{2 \times E_k}{m}} = \sqrt{\dfrac{2 \times 614\,400}{1200}} = 32$ m/s

ii) $v = \sqrt{\dfrac{2 \times E_k}{m}} = \sqrt{\dfrac{2 \times 614\,400}{12\,288}} = 10$ m/s

b) The **car** has more kinetic energy — doubling speed increases K.E. by a factor of 4 whereas trebling mass only increases K.E. by a factor of 3.

Q4 a) Distance = work done by brakes / force = 1440 ÷ 200 = **7.2 m**.

b) The temperature of the brakes increases because the kinetic energy of the wheels is transferred to the heat energy of the brakes.

Page 67 — Forces and Elasticity

Q1 a) E.g. if something is elastic it means that when a force is applied it changes its shape and stores the work as elastic potential energy. When the force is removed the elastic object can return to its original shape.

b) The kinetic energy is transferred into the elastic potential energy of the springs around the trampoline as they stretch (as well as a bit of heat and sound energy).

c) i) 600 ÷ 30 = **20 N** per spring

ii) F = k × e Rearranging gives: k = F ÷ e = 20 ÷ 0.1 = **200 N/m**.

Q2 a) F = k × e F = 45 × 15 = **675 N**

b) The limit of proportionality.

Pages 68-69 — Power

Q1 rate, energy, watts, joules, one hundred, light/ heat, heat/light

Q2 a) Power = energy ÷ time, P = E ÷ t (Or equivalent, e.g. E = P × t.)

b) Rearrange the formula to get energy = power × time. The car gets 50 000 × 5 × 60 = **15 000 000 J** of energy (= 15 000 kJ / 15 MJ).

c) Power = energy transferred ÷ time taken = 144 000 ÷ (12 × 60) = **200 W**

Q3 Gravitational potential energy = mass × g × height.

a) i) 46 × 10 × 5 = **2300 J**.

ii) 48 × 10 × 5 = **2400 J**.

b) Power = work done ÷ time Catherine's power = 2300 ÷ 6.2 = **371 W**. Sally's power = 2400 ÷ 6.4 = **375 W**. **Sally** generated more power.

Q4 a) Time in seconds = 10 × 60 = 600 s. Energy = power × time = 150 × 600 = **90 000 J** (= 90 kJ).

b) 90 kJ ÷ 30 kJ/ml = **3 ml**.

c) Power = energy ÷ time = 120 000 ÷ (10 × 60) = **200 W**

Physics 2a — Motion, Energy and Electricity

Q5 a) Josie is carrying her school bag so her total mass is 66 kg. The energy transferred by Josie is the kinetic energy she gains from her acceleration.
K.E = ½ × m × v² = 0.5 × 66 × 8² = 2112 J
Power = energy transferred ÷ time taken
= 2112 ÷ 6 = **352 W**

b) Josie puts down her school bag so her total mass is now only 60 kg. This time the energy is the gravitational potential energy she gains going up the stairs.
E_p = m × g × h = 60 × 10 × 5 = 3000 J
P = E ÷ t = 3000 J ÷ 4 = **750 W**

Q6 a) Start 4 – this wasn't a fair test because he slipped.

b) Remembering to ignore start 4 —
average time = **3.2 s**, average speed = **8.0 m/s**.

c) E.g. calculate the power for each start, e.g. for sprint 1
power = (1/2 × 70 × 8²) / 3.2 = 700 W.
Then average these powers. 2804 ÷ 4 = **701 W**.

Page 70 — Momentum and Collisions

Q1 a) If the velocity of a moving object doubles, its **momentum** will double.

b) If you drop a suitcase out of a moving car, the car's momentum will **decrease**.

c) When two objects collide the total momentum **stays the same**.

d) When a force acts on an object its momentum **changes**.

Q2 Truck A's momentum = 30 m/s × 3000 kg
= 90 000 kg m/s.
Truck B's momentum = 10 m/s × 4500 kg
= 45 000 kg m/s.
Truck C's momentum = 20 m/s × 4000 kg
= 80 000 kg m/s.
Truck D's momentum = 15 m/s × 3500 kg
= 52 500 kg m/s.
So the order of increasing momentum is: **B, D, C, A**.

Q3 a)

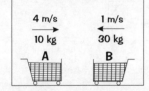

b) **Before** the collision:
Trolley A's momentum = 10 kg × 4 m/s = 40 kg m/s.
Trolley B's momentum = 30 kg × (−1 m/s) = −30 kg m/s.
(Note the minus sign for trolley B's velocity because it's travelling in the opposite direction to trolley A.)
So total momentum = 40 + (−30) = 10 kg m/s.
After the collision:
The joined trolleys have mass 40 kg and velocity v.
Momentum$_{before}$ = momentum$_{after}$ = 10 kg m/s = 40 kg × v
So, v = 10 kg m/s ÷ 40 kg = **+0.25 m/s**.
The '+' sign shows that the joined trolleys travel in the same direction that trolley A was originally moving (i.e. east).

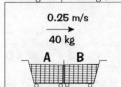

Pages 71-72 — Car Design and Safety

Q1 work, heat, regenerative, reverse, electric generator, chemical, efficient

Q2 a) Kinetic energy.

b) The brakes convert the kinetic energy into other forms of energy — mostly heat energy.

Q3 E.g. a roof box will make the car less aerodynamic and will increase the air resistance. The air resistance will therefore equal the driving force at lower speeds and the top speed will be reduced.

Q4 a) E.g. by slowing the car and passengers down over a longer period of time, you spread out the change in momentum and reduce the force that the passengers experience. OR: you decrease the size of the deceleration. This reduces the forces on the car and passengers (F = ma), leading to less severe injuries for the passengers.

b) E.g. any two from:
Crumple zones – these crumple in a collision and convert some of the car's kinetic energy into heat and sound energy as it changes shape.
Side impact bars – these direct the kinetic energy of a crash away from the passengers and towards other parts of the car, such as the crumple zones.
Airbags – transfer part of the passenger's kinetic energy to the gas inside the airbag which escapes through pores in the material. (They also prevent the passenger from hitting hard surfaces within the car.)

Q5 a) A seat belt absorbs kinetic energy as the material of the belt stretches.

b) When a car crashes it changes velocity very suddenly. This means that there is a large momentum change which can mean a very large force on the passenger. By slowing down that change in momentum, the seat belt reduces the force on the internal organs, reducing the likelihood of injury.

Q6 Convert time in hours to time in seconds:
1 hour = 60 mins = 60 × 60 s = 3600 s
P = E ÷ t = 2 650 000 000 ÷ 3600 = **736 111 W** = (736 kW)

Page 73 — Static Electricity

Q1 Circled: positive and negative, negative and positive.
Underlined: negative and negative, positive and positive.

Q2 static, insulating, friction, electrons, positive / negative, negative / positive

Q3 a) A polythene rod becomes negatively charged when rubbed with a duster because it **gains** electrons.

b) When a negatively charged object and a positively charged object are brought together, **both** the **objects exert** a force **on each other**.

c) The closer two charged objects are together, the **more** strongly they attract or repel.

d) Electrical charges **can** move very easily through metals.

Q4 Electrons are transferred between the jumper and his hair, leaving his hair electrically charged. Because all the strands of hair have the same charge they repel one another — and stand on end.

Page 74 — Current and Potential Difference

Q1 charge, voltage, work, reduces, decrease

Q2 A — Current — amps
V — Potential Difference — volts
Ω — Resistance — ohms

Q3 a) Q = I × t
t = 20 × 60 = 1200 seconds
5 × 1200 = **6000 C**

b) W = V × Q
3 × 6000 = **18 000 J** (or **18 kJ**)

Q4

	Lamp A	Lamp B
Current through lamp (A)	2	4
Voltage drop across lamp (V)	3	2
Charge passing in 10 s (C)	20	40
Work done in 10 s (J)	60	80

Physics 2a — Motion, Energy and Electricity

Q5 a) Q = I × t
4 × (7 × 60) = **1680 C**

b) W = V × Q
9 × 1680 = **15 120 J** (or **15.12 kJ**)

Page 75 — Circuits — The Basics

Q1 Cell — Provides the 'push' on the charge.

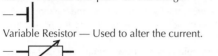

Variable Resistor — Used to alter the current.

Component — The item you're testing. —

Voltmeter — Measures the voltage. —

Ammeter — Measures the current. —

Q2 circuit, through, across

Q3 a) 1. Battery
2. Thermistor
3. Component / Fixed resistor
4. LDR
5. Switch (closed)
6. Filament Lamp

b) The ammeter must be drawn in series between the battery and the first junction.

c) The voltmeter must be drawn in parallel around the lamp.

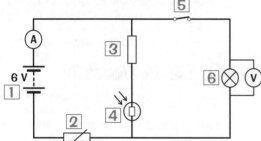

Pages 76-77 — Resistance and V = I × R

Q1 A — Filament lamp
B — Diode
C — Resistor

Q2 a) False
b) True
c) False
d) True
e) True

Q3 a) D
b) Gradient = 4 ÷ 2 = **2**.
c) Resistance = 1 ÷ gradient = 1 ÷ 2 = **0.5 Ω**.

Q4 The heat energy causes the ions in the bulb's filament to vibrate more. This makes it more difficult for charge-carrying electrons to get through the filament, so the current can't flow as easily — the resistance increases.

Q5

Voltage (V)	Current (A)	Resistance (Ω)
6	2	**3**
8	**4**	2
9	3	3
4	8	**0.5**
2	**0.5**	4
1	0.5	2

Q6 a)

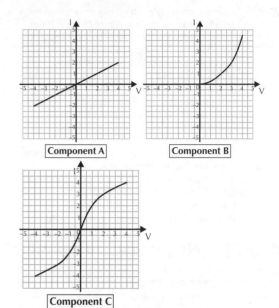

Component A

Component B

Component C

b) Resistor, diode, filament lamp

Page 78 — Circuit Devices

Q1 vary, thermistor, thermostats, light-dependent, lights

Q2 a) An LED emits light when a current flows through it in the forward direction.

b) LEDs use a much smaller current than other types of lighting (so they are cheaper to use).

Q3 a) E.g.

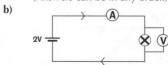

b) The resistance decreases.
c) The brightness of the lamp decreases.

Pages 79-80 — Series Circuits

Q1 Same everywhere in the circuit — Current.
Shared by all the components — Total potential difference.
The sum of the resistances — Total resistance.
Can be different for each component — Potential difference.

Q2 a) 1. The voltmeter is in series.
2. The ammeter is in parallel with the lamp.
3. The current is shown going the wrong way.
(Answers can be in any order.)

b)

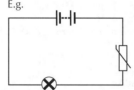

Q3 a) 2 V + 2 V + 2 V = **6 V**
b) V = I × R, so total R = total V ÷ total I = 6 ÷ 0.5 = **12 Ω**
c) R_3 = total resistance − R_1 − R_2 = 12 − 2 − 4 = **6 Ω**
d) V = I × R = 0.5 × 4 = **2 V**

Q4 a) The lamps get dimmer as more are added because the voltage is shared out between the lamps.

b) The current gets smaller as more lamps are added. Each lamp adds more resistance which means less current.

Physics 2a — Motion, Energy and Electricity

Q5 a)   E.g.

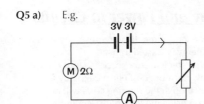

b)   It decreases

c)   Total resistance = resistance from resistor +
resistance from motor = $1\Omega + 2\Omega = 3\Omega$.
$V = I \times R$, so $I = V \div R = 6 \div 3 = \mathbf{2A}$.

Pages 81-82 — Parallel Circuits

Q1 a)   True
b)   True
c)   False
d)   True

Q2

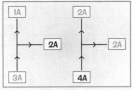

Q3   1. 6 V
2. $4\,A - 3\,A = \mathbf{1\,A}$
3. 6 V

Q4 a)   Nothing, because each lamp gets its voltage from the
battery separately.

b)   It increases because the currents to each lamp add up.

c)   Nothing happens to the brightness of the other lamps.
(The answers above assume that the internal resistance
of the cell is ignored — in practice the current would
decrease a little as lamps were added.)

Q5 a)   E.g. no, you can have a different current in each branch,
but the voltage is always the same.

b)   E.g. so that the lights can be switched on and off
independently. / So that if one light fails, the others will
still light up.

Pages 83-84 — Series and Parallel Circuits — Examples

Q1   <u>Series Circuits</u>
end to end
the same everywhere
shared between components
e.g. Christmas tree lights
<u>Parallel Circuits</u>
side by side
can be different in each branch
the same for each component
e.g. car electrics, household electrics (or any other
sensible answer)

Q2 a)   If they were wired in parallel, the bulbs would be 230 V
because each one would get the full voltage.

b)   They don't all go off if one fails / you can tell which one
has failed.

c)   The bulbs will be designed to work at different voltages.
In parallel 230 V bulbs are needed (although in practice
transformers are often used to lower the voltage). In series
the bulbs used are suitable for smaller voltages
e.g. 12 V because the voltage is shared.

Q3 $V_0 = \mathbf{12\,V}$, $A_1 = \mathbf{1\,A}$, $V_1 = I \times R = 1 \times 4 = \mathbf{4\,V}$,
$V_3 = 12\,V - 4\,V - 2\,V = \mathbf{6\,V}$

Q4 a) i) $I = V \div R = 12 \div 2 = \mathbf{6\,A}$
ii) $I = V \div R = 12 \div 4 = \mathbf{3\,A}$

b) i)   12 V
ii)   12 V
c) $A_0 = A_2 + A_3 = 3\,A + 2\,A = \mathbf{5\,A}$

Q5   1. If the engine isn't running the battery might not be able
to provide enough current for the fan and lights together at
full voltage. So the lights might be slightly dimmer.
2. If the bulbs are in series, taking one out will break the
circuit and all the bulbs will go out.
3. The wall lamps are in parallel but they share the same
switch.

Pages 85-87 — Mixed Questions — Physics 2a

Q1 a)   Work done = force × distance = 300 × 1500
= **450 000 J** (or 450 kJ).

b)   Acceleration = change in speed ÷ time taken
= $20 \div 6.2 = \mathbf{3.23\ m/s^2}$ (to 3 s.f.).

c)   This will reduce the top speed of the car — the air
resistance against the car will be increased, and so will
equal the maximum driving force at a lower speed.

d)   A seat belt will increase the time over which there is a
momentum change, so he will experience a smaller force.

Q2 a) $E_p = m \times g \times h = 12\,000 \times 34 = \mathbf{408\,000\ J}$ (= 408 kJ).

b)   Two thirds of the potential energy is converted into kinetic
energy, so gain in $E_k = 408\,000 \times 2/3$
= 272 000 J. Two thirds of the way down, speed =
$$v = \sqrt{\frac{2 \times E_k}{m}} = \sqrt{\frac{2 \times 272\,000}{1200}} = \mathbf{21.3\ m/s}\ (3\ \text{s.f.})$$

c)   Time = speed ÷ acceleration = $20 \div 6.4 = \mathbf{3.125\ s}$.

Q3 a) $10 + 5 + 5 = \mathbf{20\ \Omega}$.

b) i) $I = V \div R = 4 \div 10 = \mathbf{0.4\ A}$ (current through 10 Ω
resistor is the same as current in all parts of the circuit).

ii) $V = I \times R = 0.4 \times 20 = \mathbf{8\ V}$.

Q4 a) $120\,s - 60\,s = \mathbf{60\ s}$ (1 minute).

b)   Train 1 is faster.
Speed = gradient = $50 \div 40 = \mathbf{1.25\ m/s}$.

c)   E.g. train 1 is decelerating / has a negative
acceleration / is slowing down.

Q5 a)   No — the car is not changing speed or direction / not
accelerating and so there cannot be a resultant force.

b)   90 km/h = 90 000 ÷ 3600 = 25 m/s.
momentum = $m \times v = 2100 \times 25 = \mathbf{52\,500\ kg\,m/s}$

c) i)   E.g. how tired she is / how fast she is driving
/ whether she had consumed alcohol /
whether she had consumed drugs etc.

ii)   F = change in momentum ÷ time = 52 500 ÷ 3.0 = **17 500 N**

Q6 a) i) $4 \times 0.5 = \mathbf{2.0\ A}$.
ii)   0 A
iii) $(4 \times 0.5) + (2 \times 6.0) = \mathbf{14.0\ A}$.

b)   Thermistor — they are a temperature dependent resistor.
The resistance of a thermistor decreases as temperature
increases and increases as temperature decreases.

Q7 a)   As soon as it's dropped the dummy accelerates under
the influence of gravity. So as it falls its velocity
increases steadily. When it hits the ground its velocity
changes almost instantly to zero and stays at zero.

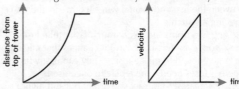

b) i)   Work done = potential energy gained
= $m \times g \times h = 95 \times 10 \times 60 = \mathbf{57\,000\ J}$ (or 57 kJ).

ii)   Time = work ÷ power = 57 000 ÷ 760 = **75 s**.

c)   Weight of dummy = $m \times g = 95 \times 10 = 950\ N$
$k = F \div e = 950 \div 5 = \mathbf{190\ N/m}$

Q8 a)   her weight / gravity
b)   700 N

Physics 2b — Electricity and the Atom

c) There is now a resultant force on her, acting upwards. This accelerates her upwards, reducing her downward velocity.
d) 700 N

Physics 2b — Electricity and the Atom

Page 88 — Mains Electricity

Q1 volts, alternating, a.c., direction, changing, frequency, hertz, batteries, direct, d.c., same
Q2 a) C
b) B
c) A
Q3 a) 2 volts
b) 4×10 ms = **40 ms** or **0.04 s**
c) Frequency = $1 \div 0.04$ = **25 Hz**

Page 89 — Electricity in the Home

Q1 There should be rings round: cable over cooker, overloaded socket, cable over sink, sockets too near the sink, long cable on the floor, hamster chewing the cable, child sitting on worktop sticking a fork in the socket, lamp that could easily be knocked over.
Q2 a) Because these materials are electrical insulators.
b) These materials are electrical conductors, and are used for those parts that the electricity goes through.
c) Rubber or plastic because they are electrical insulators and are flexible.
Q3 a) insulation
b) live
c) neutral
d) green and yellow, earth
e) firmly, bare
f) outer
Q4 1. The earth wire isn't connected.
2. Bare wires are showing.
3. The neutral and live wires are the wrong way round.

Page 90 — Fuses and Earthing

Q1 The live and neutral wires should normally carry the same current.
A circuit breaker does the same job as a fuse.
A Residual Current Circuit Breaker can be used instead of a fuse and earth wire.
Any metal casing should be connected to the earth wire.
A fuse melts when the current in a fuse wire exceeds the rating of the fuse.
Q2 1. A fault allows the live wire to touch the metal case.
2. A big current flows out through the earth wire.
3. A big surge in current blows the fuse.
4. The device is isolated from the live wire.
Q3 a) When an RCCB detects a difference in the current between the live and neutral wires it turns off the power by opening a switch.
b) E.g. any two from: They work much faster than fuses. / They work even for small current changes that might not be large enough to melt a fuse. / They can easily be reset whereas fuses need to be replaced once used.
Q4 a) **2 A.** (It's nearest to the actual current but still higher so that it won't blow with normal use.)
b) Because it has an insulated case with no metal parts showing.
c) two-core cable
d) They both increase with current size — the bigger the current, the higher the fuse rating needs to be and the thicker the cable needs to be to carry it.

Page 91 — Energy and Power in Circuits

Q1 how long, power, energy, time, heat, more
Q2 a) E.g. most of the energy is wasted as heat.
b) E.g. it's more energy efficient (so cheaper to run).
c) E.g. he might think it is more cost effective to buy a cheaper bulb even though the running costs will be more (he may not plan on using the light bulb very much).
Q3 a) 1000 J, light, heat
b) 60 000 J, kinetic, heat, sound
c) 20 000 J, heat
d) 1 200 000 J, heat

Page 92 — Power and Energy Change

Q1 a)

	Lamp A	Lamp B	Lamp C
Voltage (V)	12	3	230
Current (A)	2.5	4	0.1
Power (W)	30	12	23
Energy used in one minute (J)	1800	720	1380

b) A = 3 A, B = 5 A, C = 1 A.
Q2 a) Current = power ÷ voltage = $1500 \div 230$ = 6.5 A
b) 7 A
Q3

	Drill A	Drill B
Current through drill (A)	2	3
Voltage drop across drill (V)	230	230
Charge passing in 5 s (C)	10	15
Energy transformed in 5 s (J)	2300	3450

Q4 a) $Q = I \times t$
$0.6 \times (12 \times 60)$ = **432 C**
b) $W = V \times Q$
2×432 = **864 J**

Page 93 — Atomic Structure

Q1 a) no
b) ion
c) protons, electrons (in either order)
d) positively
Q2

Particle	Mass	Charge
Proton	1	+1
Neutron	1	0
Electron	very small	−1

Q3 a) i) They fired a beam of alpha particles at thin gold foil.
ii) They expected the positively charged alpha particles to be slightly deflected by the electrons in the plum pudding model.
b) Most of the alpha particles went straight through the foil, but the odd one came straight back at them. This showed that atoms are not like a plum pudding, they have a very small central nucleus with electrons orbiting round it. The nucleus must have a large positive charge as it repelled the positive alpha particles by large angles. Most of the atom is empty space — the nucleus is tiny compared to the size of the atom.

Pages 94-95 — Atoms and Ionising Radiation

Q1 a) False
b) True
c) False
d) False
e) True

Physics 2b — Electricity and the Atom

Q2 a) i) Background radiation.
  ii) E.g. any two from: Nuclear weapon tests. / Nuclear accidents. / Dumped nuclear waste.
  b) i) Background radiation is higher in Cornwall due to the type of rock underground.
  ii) E.g. any one from: food / cosmic rays / building materials.
  iii) Yes. $(1000 \times 0.00001) + 0.008 = 0.018$.
Q3 Alpha particle — 2 neutrons and 2 protons — the same as a helium nucleus.
Beta particle — An electron from the nucleus.
Gamma radiation — A type of electromagnetic radiation.
Q4

Radiation Type	Ionising power weak/moderate/strong	Charge positive/none/negative	Relative mass no mass/small/large	Penetrating power low/moderate/high	Range in air short/long/very long
alpha	strong	positive	large	low	short
beta	moderate	negative	small	moderate	long
gamma	weak	none	no mass	high	very long

Q5 a) $^{234}_{90}\text{Th} \rightarrow \, ^{234}_{91}\text{Pa} + \, ^{0}_{-1}\text{e}$
  b) $^{222}_{86}\text{Rn} \rightarrow \, ^{218}_{84}\text{Po} + \, ^{4}_{2}\alpha$
Q6 1. The particles move in opposite directions — this is because they have opposite charges.
2. The alpha particle is deflected less than the beta particle — this is because alpha particles have a much greater mass than beta particles.

Page 96 — Half-Life

Q1 In 60 years' time, the count rate will be half what it is now.
Q2 a) In 29 years time, the count rate will have halved — half of the radioactive nuclei will have decayed.
  b) **125** (87 years is 3 half-lives.)
Q3 After 1 half-life: 720 cpm
After 2 half-lives: 360 cpm
After 3 half-lives: 180 cpm
After 4 half-lives: 90 cpm
After 5 half-lives: 45 cpm
Therefore 5 hours is 5 half-lives.
So 1 half-life = **1 hour**.
Q4 a)

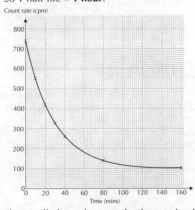

  b) There will always be some background radiation (in this case it looks like approx. 100 cpm) AND the radioactivity of the sample will never fall to zero.
  c) The background radiation must be subtracted from her readings. The count therefore starts at 640. Half of that is 320 (or 420 including background radiation). This occurs on the 20th minute.

Page 97 — Uses of Radiation

Q1 1. The radioactive source emits alpha particles.
2. The air between the electrodes is ionised by the alpha particles.
3. A current flows between the electrodes — the alarm stays off.
4. A fire starts and smoke particles absorb the alpha radiation.
5. The circuit is broken so no current flows.
6. The alarm sounds.
Q2 a) A gamma-emitter with a long half-life is used. Gamma radiation is needed because it is not stopped by air or metal parts of the instruments and can kill the cells of living organisms (e.g. bacteria) on the instruments. A long half-life is needed because the sterilising machine will be in use over many years and replacing the source frequently would be inconvenient.
  b) Lead is used to prevent the operator and anyone near the machine from getting too high a dose of radiation.
Q3 a) Technetium-99. It has the shortest half-life.
  b) Cobalt-60. It emits gamma radiation, which can penetrate the body and can kill cancer cells. It has a fairly long half-life so the hospital would not need to replace the source too often.

Page 98 — Radioactivity Safety

Q1 a) E.g. he isn't wearing protective gloves. He isn't using tongs to handle the sample. He is pointing the sample directly into the face of the other scientist.
  b) E.g. by minimising the time the samples are out of their boxes.
  c) In a thick-walled, lead-lined container.
Q2 a) beta and gamma
  b) i) alpha radiation
  ii) It's highly ionising and can damage or kill cells in our bodies. A high dose can kill lots of cells at once, causing radiation sickness. It can also cause cancer when cells are damaged, mutate and divide uncontrollably.

Page 99 — Nuclear Fission and Fusion

Q1 uranium-235, split, heat, water, steam, turbine, generator, electricity
Q2 E.g. the slow-moving neutron is absorbed by a plutonium nucleus. This plutonium nucleus splits up, forming new lighter elements and spitting out two or three neutrons. One or more of these 'extra' neutrons may then be absorbed by another plutonium nucleus, causing it to split and spit out more neutrons, which may cause other nuclei to split etc.
Q3 E.g. any four from: Fission splits nuclei up, fusion combines nuclei. / Fission reactors use uranium or plutonium, fusion reactors use hydrogen. / Fission produces radioactive waste, fusion produces very little radioactive waste. / Fission reactors already exist, fusion reactors are still being developed. / Fusion requires extremely high temperatures, fission does not.
Q4 **Good points**
E.g. fuel is cheap and plentiful, they produce very little radioactive waste.
Bad points
E.g. no materials can stand the high temperatures needed, it requires a lot of energy to achieve such high temperatures.

Pages 100-101 — The Life Cycle of Stars

Q1 hot, fusion, stable, outwards, inwards, billions
Q2 a) Gravitational attraction pulls the material together.
  b) Gas and dust in orbit around a newly formed star may clump together to form masses. The smaller masses are attracted to larger masses, and they eventually merge together to become planets.

Q3 a) A star becomes a red giant when the hydrogen fuel in its core begins to run out. (Hydrogen outside the core is burnt, heating the outer layers and causing the star to expand.)

b) It becomes red because its surface cools.

c) They cool and contract into a white dwarf and then when the light fades completely they become a black dwarf.

Q4 The explosion is called a supernova. The outer layers of dust and gas are thrown out into the universe. This leaves a very dense core known as a neutron star. If the star is big enough this can become a black hole.

Q5 A Clouds of Dust and Gas   B Protostar
C Main Sequence Star   D Red Giant
E White Dwarf   F Black Dwarf
G Red Super Giant   H Supernova
I Neutron Star   J Black Hole

Q6 a) New elements have been formed by fusion in stars.

b) They consume massive amounts of hydrogen.

c) They are formed when a big star explodes in a supernova and are ejected into the universe.

Pages 102-104 — Mixed Questions — Physics 2b

Q1 a) The nucleus of cobalt-60 contains one more neutron than that of cobalt-59.

b) medical tracers — technetium-99m
smoke detectors — americium-241
detecting leaks in pipes — technetium-99m or cobalt-60

c) i) gamma

ii) Because the radiation damages healthy normal cells as well as the cancerous ones.

d) Work out how many half-lives would be needed.
$120 \div 2^5 = 3.75$, so just under 5 half-lives would be needed to bring the count rate down to 4 cpm.
The half-life of americium-241 is 432 years.
$432 \times 5 = 2160$. So roughly **2000 years** would be needed.

e) Any two of: always handle the source with tongs. / Never allow the source to touch his skin. / Hold the source as far away from his body as possible. / Keep the source pointing away from his body. / Avoid looking directly at the source. / Store the source in a lead-lined box and put it away as soon as his experiment is finished.

Q2 a) nuclear fission

b) A neutron hits a uranium nucleus and is absorbed, giving the nucleus too many neutrons to be stable. It then decays into two smaller nuclei and some fast-moving neutrons, which go on to cause other uranium nuclei to undergo fission.

c) The heat from the reactor is used to make steam, which turns a turbine attached to a generator, which produces the electricity.

d) E.g. doesn't produce radioactive waste, there's plenty of hydrogen around to use as fuel.

e) At the moment it takes more power to create the right conditions in a reactor needed for fusion (e.g. high temperature) than the reactor can produce.

f) i) Stars consume huge amounts of hydrogen in nuclear fusion (which creates new elements).

ii) Heat created by nuclear fusion provides an outward pressure to balance the force of gravity pulling everything inwards.

Q3 a) A large current flows through the live wire, passes through the metal case and out down the earth wire. The large current causes the fuse to melt, which cuts off the live supply.

b) i) live, neutral

ii) It doesn't need an earth wire because the case is made of plastic and there are no metal parts exposed or which could touch the case.

Q4 a) A current that always keeps flowing in the same direction.

b) $I = P \div V = 600 \div 230 = 2.6$ (to 2 s.f)
So the fuse needed is a 3 A fuse.

c) The broken plastic casing may expose live parts which could give Kate an electric shock.

d) Time period = $10 \text{ ms} \times 3.5 = 0.01 \times 3.5 = 0.035$ s
Frequency = $1 \div 0.035 = $ **29 Hz**.

Physics 3a — Medical Applications of Physics

Pages 105-106 — X-rays in Medicine

Q1 a) short, ionisation

b) transmitted, absorbed

c) charge-coupled device

d) atom

Q2 kill, cells, cancer, focused, normal, ill, rotating, centre

Q3 a) E.g. X-rays interact with photographic film in the same way as visible light. The X-ray image is formed by the varying intensities of X-ray beam that are transmitted (i.e. through soft tissue) through to the film. Where the X-rays are transmitted, more X-rays reach the photographic plate causing it to turn dark. This leaves a white image of the denser areas.

b) E.g. A charge-coupled device can be used to form a high resolution image. A CCD is a grid of millions of pixels, each of which is sensitive to X-rays. Each pixel generates an electric signal when it interacts with an X-ray.

c) E.g. bone fractures.

Q4 a) True

b) False

c) False

d) True

Q5 1. The patient is put inside the CT scanner.
2. An X-ray tube emits an X-ray beam whilst rotating around the patient.
3. Detectors on the opposite side of the scanner measure the intensity of the transmitted X-rays.
4. A computer uses the detected X-rays to generate an image of a two-dimensional slice through the body.
5. Multiple slice images are put together to give a three-dimensional picture.

Q6 a) E.g. any two from: wear a lead apron / stand behind a lead screen / leave the room.

b) E.g. any two from: minimise exposure time / avoid repeat X-rays / use lead to shield other areas of the body not being imaged.

Page 107 — Ultrasound

Q1 a) Ultrasound is sound with a frequency above 20 000 Hz — higher than the upper limit of hearing for humans.

b) Electrical devices can be set to produce electrical oscillations at the required frequency. These can be converted into mechanical vibrations (i.e. sound waves).

Q2 E.g.

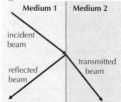

Q3 a) Looking at the oscilloscope trace, there is a 5 μs gap between the start of the trace and the first ultrasound pulse.
$s = v \times t$
$v = 1450$ m/s, $t = 0.000005$ s
$s = 1450 \times 0.000005 = 0.00725$
You need to divide by 2 to find the distance between the ultrasound device and the fat boundary:
$0.00725 \div 2 = $ **0.003625 m** (= 0.36 cm).

b) The time between traces = 5×5 μs = 0.000025 s
Distance = speed × time = 1450×0.000025 = 0.03625 m
But this is the distance to travel through the layer of fat and back again so divide by 2 to find the thickness of the layer of fat: $0.03625 \div 2 = 0.018125$ m = **1.8 cm** (to 1 d.p.)

Page 108 — Ultrasound Uses

Q1 a) It breaks the kidney stones into small particles.
b) They pass out of the body in urine.
c) E.g. it's relatively painless, no surgery is required.
Q2 a)

	Advantage	Disadvantage
Ultrasound imaging	E.g. non-ionising, can image soft tissue	E.g. produces low resolution, fuzzy images
X-ray photographs	E.g. low radiation dose, can image hard tissue, e.g. bone, better resolution than ultrasound images	E.g. the radiation is ionising, images are limited to 2D
CT scans	E.g. produces high resolution images of both hard and soft tissue, can be used to make 3D images	E.g. high radiation dose, expensive

b) E.g. CT scanning, because a high resolution image of both the brain and the skull can be produced.
Q3 a) Ultrasound causes no known damage to cells, whereas X-rays are ionising radiation which can cause cancer.
b) X-rays — they penetrate most of the soft tissues but are absorbed (mostly) by bone. Ultrasound would not give a good picture of the bone as it would be reflected at the boundaries between different layers of soft tissue.

Page 109 — Refractive Index

Q1 a) refraction
b) E.g.

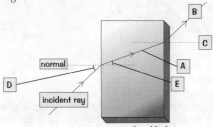

glass block

Q2 a) The ratio of the speed of light in a vacuum to the speed of light in that medium.
b) n = sin i / sin r
n = refractive index, i = angle of incidence, r = angle of refraction.
Q3 n = sin 30 ÷ sin 22 = **1.3**.
Q4 n = sin i / sin r, so 1.514 = sin 45 ÷ sin r.
Therefore sin r = sin 45 ÷ 1.514 = 0.467.
Hence r = $\sin^{-1}$(0.467) = **27.8°**.

Pages 110-111 — Lenses and Images

Q1 a) W = incident
X = converging
Y = parallel
Z = focal point
b) The following statements should be ticked:
Any ray passing along the axis
Any ray passing through the centre of the lens
Q2 a) False
b) True
c) True
d) False
Q3 a) D — Either a converging or a diverging lens

b)

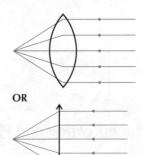

OR

Q4 a) In a real image, the rays from the object actually pass through the image (so it can be projected onto a screen). In a virtual image, the rays only appear to have come from the location of the image.
b) 1. say its size
2. say whether it is upright or inverted
3. say whether it is real or virtual.
Q5 a) The focal point on the other side of the lens.
b) Through the centre of the lens.
c) The top of the image will be where those two rays meet.
Q6

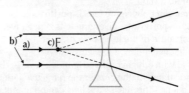

Pages 112-113 — Lenses

Q1

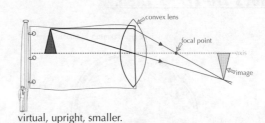

Q2 virtual, upright, smaller.
Q3 a)

Distance from lens to object	Distance from lens to image	Type of image	Size of image
Greater than 2F	Between 2F and F	Real, inverted	Smaller than object
Equal to 2F	**Equal to 2F**	Real, inverted	**Equal to object**
Between 2F and F	Greater than 2F	**Real, inverted**	**Larger than object**
Less than F	Greater than 2F	**Virtual, upright**	Larger than object

b) i) The image will be 1 cm high.
ii) The image will be 5 cm away from the lens on the opposite side from the object.
Q4 a) i) upright
ii) on the same side
iii) virtual
b) C – 10.2 cm
Q5

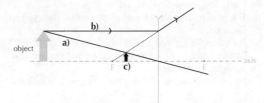

Physics 3a — Medical Applications of Physics

Q6

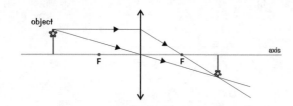

Pages 114-115 — Magnification and Power

Q1 a) A convex / converging lens

b) It is only at a distance nearer than the focal point that you will get an upright, magnified, virtual image.

c) B, D and E should be circled.

Q2 a) Magnification = image height ÷ object height

b) M = 0.8 ÷ 0.5 = 1.6

c) 3 × 1.6 = 4.8 mm

Q3 a) fatter lenses

b) power = 1 ÷ focal length

Q4 a) power = 1 ÷ focal length = 1 ÷ 0.15
= **6.67 D** (to 2 d.p.)

b) focal length = 1 ÷ power = 1 ÷ 5.2
= **0.19 m** (to 2 d.p.)

c) The **power** of a converging lens is **positive**, whereas the **power** of a diverging lens is **negative**.

Q5 a) 1. The curvature of the lens surfaces.
2. The refractive index of the lens material.

b) A material with a higher refractive index was used. For a given focal length, the greater the refractive index the flatter the lens. This means the lens can be manufactured to be thinner.

Pages 116-117 — The Eye

Q1

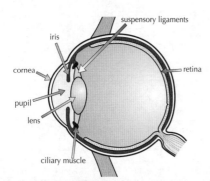

Q2a) Both are real, inverted images projected onto a "screen" (the film in the case of the camera, the retina in the case of the eye).

b) Because for an object nearer to a converging lens than the focal length, the image formed is virtual. A virtual image can't be projected onto the film.

c) on the film, smaller, retina

Q3

Part of the eye	Function
Lens	Focuses light on the retina
Retina	Light sensitive layer
Ciliary muscles	Cause the lens to change shape
Pupil	Hole through which light enters the eye

Q4 relax, thin, cornea, retina, retina

Q5 a) The near point is **the closest distance that the eye can focus on.**
For normally-sighted adults, the near point is about **25** cm.

b) The far point is **the furthest distance that the eye can focus on comfortably.**
For normally-sighted adults, the far point is at **infinity**.

Page 118 — Correcting Vision

Q1 a) short, far, far away, in front of

b) 1. Cornea and lens system is too powerful.
2. Eyeball is too long.

c) i) A

ii) A diverging lens of negative power compensates for an overly powerful lens and cornea system. The light from the object is diverged before it enters the eye so that the image is brought into focus at the retina. It makes objects an infinite distance away appear as though they are at the eye's natural far point.

Q2 a) A narrow intense beam of light.

b) i) To burn and seal shut tissue, e.g. blood vessels.

ii) E.g. a surgeon uses a laser to vaporise some of the cornea to change its shape. This can increase or decrease the power of the cornea, and so correct long or short sight.

Page 119 — Total Internal Reflection

Q1 a) Visible light.

b) Glass or perspex/plastic.

c) One bundle brings the light to the area/object in the body that needs to be looked at. The second bundle brings the light from the area/object back to form an image so the area can be viewed.

d) In the left-hand diagram, the angle of incidence is 46° (greater than the critical angle of 42°), so the ray is totally internally reflected. In the second diagram, the angle of incidence is 30°, so the ray is partially reflected, but most of the light passes out of the glass.

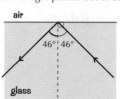 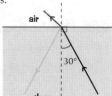

Q2 a) n = 1 ÷ sin c, c = 42°
n = 1 ÷ sin 42 **= 1.49**

b) c = sin⁻¹ (1 ÷ n), n = 2.4
c = sin⁻¹ (1 ÷ 2.4) **= 24.6°**

c) The diamond ring will be the most sparkly because it has the smaller critical angle, and so will totally internally reflect light from more angles than glass.

Pages 120-122 — Mixed Questions — Physics 3a

Q1 a) i) Medium 1 is glass
Medium 2 is air

ii) The light ray bends away from the normal as it enters medium 2, which shows its speed has increased. Light will speed up as it enters a less dense medium, which means medium 2 must be air.

b) i) B

ii) Total internal reflection occurs when light is travelling from a dense medium to a less dense medium. B is true because the light is travelling from glass to air — air is less dense than glass.

c) i) n = 1 ÷ sin c, c = 49°, n = 1 ÷ sin 49 **= 1.33**

ii) n = sin i ÷ sin r, rearranging gives:
sin r = sin i ÷ n, r = sin⁻¹ (sin i ÷ n)
n = 1.33, i = 20°
r = sin⁻¹ (sin 20 ÷ 1.33) **= 14.9°** (to 1 d.p.)

Physics 3b — Forces and Electromagnetism

Q2 a)

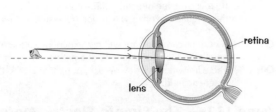

retina

lens

b) short, behind, convex
c) i) Power = 1 ÷ focal length = 1 ÷ 0.4 = **2.5 D**
   ii) The left lens is more powerful so will have a more strongly curved surface (the more curved the lens the greater its power).
d) i) 3 cm
   ii) 4 ÷ 1.8 = 2.2
   iii) Virtual — the light rays don't actually come from where they appear to, and the image can't be projected on a screen.
Q3 a) v = 1500 m/s
   d = v × t = 1500 × 0.0000260 = 0.039 m
   0.039 ÷ 2 = 0.0195 m ≈ **2 cm**.
b) E.g. X-rays are ionising and are therefore dangerous to the developing fetus. Ultrasound is non-ionising and, as far as anyone can tell, safe. (Ultrasound can image soft tissue whereas X-rays are more suited to imaging dense or hard tissue such as bone.)
c) E.g. X-rays are used to treat cancer because they are ionising. Large doses of ionising radiation can be used to kill cancerous cells. Ultrasound is non-ionising and won't damage cancerous cells.
d) E.g. CT scans use large doses of ionising X-rays which can be damaging to the health of the patient.
e) E.g. an **X-ray tube** fires intense beams of X-rays through the patient. These X-rays are picked up by **detectors** on the opposite side. The X-ray tube and detectors are **rotated** during the scan and a **computer** interprets the different intensities of X-ray signals to form an image of a two-dimensional **slice** of the patient. Multiple two-dimensional CT scans are compiled by the computer to form a three-dimensional image.

Physics 3b — Forces and Electromagnetism

Pages 123-124 — Turning Forces and the Centre of Mass

Q1 a) force, moment, perpendicular, pivot.
b) Nm (newton-metres)
Q2 a) M = F × d = 45 × 0.1 = 4.5 Nm
b) i) B
   ii) C
Q3 a)

The centre of mass must fall on this line

b) centre of mass, vertically below, perpendicular, moment.
Q4 a)

The lines should pass through the middle of each side

b) D

Q5 The weight of the pole acts at its centre of mass. The centre of mass of the pole is 0.4 m from each end. So the weight of 130 N acts 0.4 m from the pivot.
M = F × d = 130 × 0.4 = 52 Nm
Q6 a) Hang the plumb line from the same point as the piece of card. Draw a pencil line on the card along the plumb line. Hang the card in a different position and do the same thing again.
Where the two lines cross is the centre of mass.
b) Preferred answer: Repeat the same steps for several pivot points to get multiple lines that will all cross at the centre of mass.
Other acceptable answers: make sure the card is not swaying when the lines are marked / is not moved by marking the lines
/ is not bent out of shape; make sure the line isn't too thick
and is accurately placed.

Page 125 — Balanced Moments and Levers

Q1 a) M = F × d = 2 × 0.2 = 0.4 Nm anticlockwise.
b) M = F × d = 5 × 0.16 = 0.8 Nm anticlockwise.
c) Total anticlockwise moments = total clockwise moments.
0.4 Nm + 0.8 Nm = 8 N × distance
1.2 Nm = 8 N × distance
1.2 ÷ 8 = distance
distance = 0.15 m = 15 cm.
d) No. Since all the moments would be multiplied by 2, it would stay balanced.
Q2 E.g. The wheelbarrow reduces the amount of force needed to give a particular moment. It does this by having long handles which mean that less force is needed to lift the wheelbarrow, as the point at which the force is applied is further away from the pivot (M = F × d).
Q3 The weight acts at the centre of mass = 40 cm from the pivot. The leg is 80 − 5 = 75 cm from the pivot.
Anticlockwise moments = Clockwise moments
40 N × 0.4 m = F × 0.75 m
16 Nm = F × 0.75 m
16 ÷ 0.75 = F
F = 21.3 N

Page 126 — Moments, Stability and Pendulums

Q1 A lot of the mass of the filing cabinet is concentrated in the top draw. So, when the drawer is fully pulled out, the centre of mass could move beyond the edge of the base, making the cabinet unstable.
Q2 C. Because it has the widest base and lowest centre of mass.
Q3 a) The line of action of the weight lies inside the base of the cart.
b) E.g. Having a wider/heavier base to lower the centre of mass.
Q4 a) f = 1 ÷ T, so T = 1 ÷ f = 1 ÷ 1.25 = **0.8 Hz**
b) Increase the length of the pendulum.

Page 127 — Hydraulics

Q1 flow, incompressible, force, transmitted, pressure, equally
Q2 a) They use different cross-sectional areas for the effort and load. P = F ÷ A, so a pressure is created at the first piston using a small force over a small area. Pressure is transmitted equally through a liquid, so the pressure at the second piston is the same. The second piston has a larger area — so there will be a much larger force acting on it.
b) i) P = F ÷ A = 650 ÷ 0.0025 = **260 000 Pa** (or N/m²)

Physics 3b — Forces and Electromagnetism

ii)   The pressure will be the same (260 000 Pa) because pressure is transmitted equally through a liquid — so the pressure at both pistons will be the same.

Q3 a)   P = F ÷ A = 18 ÷ 0.00012 = **150 000 Pa** (or N/m²)

b)   Pressure at smaller piston = pressure at larger piston, so
F = P × A = 150 000 × 0.0003 = **45 N**

Page 128 — Circular Motion

Q1   D — a change in velocity

Q2 a) and b)

Q3 a)   Yes. It is continually changing direction, so it must be changing velocity — accelerating.

b)   The following statements should be ticked:
"If a body is accelerating then there must be a resultant force acting on it."
"If there is no resultant force acting on a body then it carries on moving in a straight line at the same speed."

c)   Centripetal force

d)   A runner running round a circular track — Friction
A satellite in orbit round the Earth — Gravity
The seats at the ends of the spokes of a spinning fairground ride — Tension

Q4 a)   greater

b)   greater

c)   1617 N

Pages 129-130 — Magnetic Fields

Q1   Magnetic fields can exert a force on a wire carrying a current.

Q2

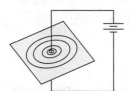

Q3 a)   It would exert a force of attraction on it.

b)   electromagnet

Q4   E.g. Unlike ordinary magnets, electromagnets are magnets which can be switched on and off. So they're useful for attracting and picking up magnetic materials (e.g. iron) so they can be moved, but they can then be made to drop the materials by switching off the current.

Q5 a)   When the switch is closed the right-hand contact is attracted towards the solenoid. This breaks the external circuit, turning it off. When the switch is turned off, the solenoid loses its magnetism and the contact is returned to its original position by the spring. This turns the external circuit on again.

b)   The soft iron core makes the solenoid more powerful / It has a stronger magnetic force. Soft iron will lose its magnetism quickly when the electric current is switched off.

Page 131 — The Motor Effect

Q1   magnetic field, permanent magnets, force, current, stronger, angle, motor

Q2 a)   The wire will move out of the paper (towards the reader).

b)   By reversing the direction of the current OR by turning the magnets the other way round (reversing the magnetic field).

Q3   A current-carrying wire will not experience a force if it is parallel to the magnetic field of a permanent magnet.

Q4   The wire will move downwards, at right angles to the magnetic field.

Page 132 — The Simple Electric Motor

Q1   Using a commutator.

Q2   The split-ring commutator reverses the direction of the current every half turn by swapping the contacts to the DC supply.

Q3   By reversing the polarity of the magnets OR by reversing the direction of the current.

Q4   E.g. the axle of the electric motor could be used to turn a (large) pulley wheel, around which the lift cables could wind or unwind to raise or lower the lift.

Q5   current, magnetic, field, force, amplifier, move, frequency, sound.

Page 133 — Electromagnetic Induction

Q1 a)   E.g. Electromagnetic induction is the creation of a potential difference across the ends of a conductor which is experiencing a change in magnetic field (as it 'cuts' through magnetic field lines).

b)   Move the (vertical) wire in and out of the magnetic field at an angle to the direction of the field (i.e. not parallel to the magnetic field).

c)   The ammeter needle would move first in one direction, then back to zero and then in the opposite direction and back to zero again. It would continue like this as long as the wire was moving in and out of the magnetic field.

d)   The ammeter needle would still move from one side to the other, but would start from the opposite side.

Q2 a)   By pulling the magnet out again OR by turning the magnet round and pushing it into the coil OR by pushing the magnet into the coil from the left-hand side OR by turning the magnet around and pulling it out of the left-hand side of the coil.

b)   By pushing the magnet in and immediately pulling it out again.

c)   By rapidly pushing the magnet in and out of the coil a number of times.

Q3   E.g. The cog wheel is attached to the bicycle wheel. The cog is attached to a magnet — as the wheel turns, the cog turns and rotates the magnet in a coil of wire on a soft iron core. This induces a potential difference in the coil and a current flows in the wire. The coil is connected in a circuit with the light bulb and so the bulb lights up.

Pages 134-137 — Transformers

Q1   1. A source of alternating potential difference is applied to the primary coil.
2. An alternating current flows in the primary coil.
3. This produces an alternating magnetic field in the iron core.
4. The magnetic field produced inside the secondary coil induces an alternating potential difference at the ends of the secondary coil.
5. If this is applied to an external circuit, an alternating current will flow in that circuit.

Physics 3b — Forces and Electromagnetism

Q2 a) When a current flows in the left-hand coil it generates a magnetic field which induces a current in the right hand coil and causes the needle of the ammeter to deflect. Since a current can only be induced when the magnetic field changes, the deflection only occurs when the current is switched on or off.

b) You could put an iron core through the two coils / add more turns to the coils / add more cells to the battery etc. This would make the magnetic field stronger and therefore cause bigger deflections in the ammeter.

Q3 True, false, true.

Q4 A step-down transformer.

Q5 a) A transformer consists of an iron core and two coils.

b) Step-up transformers have more turns on the secondary coil than the primary coil.

c) In a step-down transformer the potential difference across the secondary coil is less than the potential difference across the primary coil.
OR
In a step-up transformer the potential difference across the secondary coil is greater than the potential difference across the primary coil.

Q6 a) The alternating current produces an alternating magnetic field in the core, which in turn induces an alternating potential difference in the secondary coil.

b) Only an alternating current can produce the constantly-changing magnetic field needed to continually induce a voltage in the secondary coil.

Q7 Ash is **wrong** because the iron core carries magnetic field, not current.

Q8 a) True, true, false, true.

b) E.g. any one from: mobile phone chargers / power supplies.

Q9 a) It is a step-down transformer — it reduces the voltage from 240 V to 12 V.

b) i) $P = V \times I = 240 \times 0.25 = \textbf{60 W}$.

ii) $P = V \times I = 12 \times 5 = \textbf{60 W}$.

c) Transformers are nearly 100% efficient.

Q10 The number of turns increases by a factor of 40 so the voltage will also increase by a factor of 40. So the input voltage would need to be $10\,000 \div 40 = \textbf{250 V}$.
Alternatively, use the equation:

$$\frac{V_p}{V_s} = \frac{N_p}{N_s}, \quad \frac{V_p}{10\,000} = \frac{100}{4000}, \quad V_p = \frac{10\,000 \times 100}{4000} = \textbf{250 V}.$$

Q11

Number of turns on primary coil	Voltage to primary coil (V)	Number of turns on secondary coil	Voltage to secondary coil (V)
1000	12	4000	**48**
1000	**10**	2000	20
1000	12	**1000**	12
71 739	33 000	500	230

Q12 a) Output voltage = $230\,\text{V} \times (8000/5000) = \textbf{368 V}$.

b) $230 \div 20 = 11.5$. So there must be 11.5 times more turns on the primary coil than on the secondary. Andy could either:
Keep 5000 turns on the primary coil and adapt the **secondary coil** to have $5000 \div 11.5 = \textbf{435 turns}$.
OR
Keep 8000 turns on the secondary coil and adapt the **primary coil** to have $8000 \times 11.5 = \textbf{92 000 turns}$.

Q13 $V_p \times I_p = V_s \times I_s$
So, $I_p = (V_s \times I_s) \div V_p = (110 \times 20) \div 230 = \textbf{9.6 A}$

Pages 138-140 — Mixed Questions — Physics 3b

Q1 a) Anticlockwise moment = $1000 \times 0.6 = 600\,\text{Nm}$
$F = 600 \div 1.8 = \textbf{333 N}$

b) The wheelbarrow was tilted so its **centre of mass** moved beyond the edge of its base. This caused a **resultant moment**, causing the wheelbarrow to tip.

c) E.g. the position of the centre of mass, width of the base.

Q2 a) $f = 1 \div T = 1 \div 2 = \textbf{0.5 Hz}$

b) The force applied to the water at the top of the bag is transmitted to water in other parts of the bag, and causes water to squirt out of the hole.

c) E.g. The large piston has a greater cross-sectional area than the small piston. A small force is applied to the small piston to create a pressure on a liquid. Pressure is transmitted equally through a liquid, so the pressure is the same at the large piston. $F = P \times A$, so there will be a larger force at the larger piston.

Q3 a) The iron core increases the strength of the magnetic field produced by the current in the solenoid.

b) When the switch is closed the electromagnet is turned on, setting up a magnetic field. The iron rocker is attracted towards the electromagnet, so it pivots. This closes the contacts in the motor's circuit and turns the motor on.

Q4 a) The motion tells you which way the forces must be acting — see below.

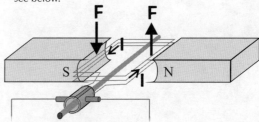

b) Use Fleming's Left-Hand Rule on one side of the coil. E.g. for the right-hand side of the coil, the field (first finger) goes from right to left (north to south), the motion (thumb) goes upwards, giving you the current (second finger) going into the page.

c) E.g. increase the current, use a stronger magnet.

Q5 a) An alternating potential difference is induced because the coil experiences a magnetic field which is changing (and 'cutting' through the coil).

b) The induced potential difference would be in the opposite direction (when the magnet is at any given position).

Q6 a) gravity

b) i) False

ii) False

c) A

Q7 a) Ratio of turns (secondary:primary) is 200:1000 = 1:5. So the output voltage will be $230 \div 5 = \textbf{46 V}$.

b) i) Iron.

ii) It transfers the magnetic field from the primary to the secondary coil.

c) $33\,\text{kV} = 33\,000\,\text{V}$. Then:
Secondary voltage/Primary voltage = $230/33\,000$. So No. of turns on secondary coil = $2000 \times 230 \div 33\,000$ = 14 turns.

d) E.g. they are lighter and smaller than traditional transformers and so are useful for lightweight devices like chargers. They are also more efficient, as they don't use much power when plugged in but have no load (i.e. a mobile phone) attached.

ISBN 978 1 84762 629 5

9 781847 626295

PAA46